Elsie's Wa

Carol MacLean lives in the Glasgow area. She began by writing pocket novels, having 18 published before deciding to write historical saga. When she's not writing, Carol can be found visiting museums or walking around the city looking for traces of old Glasgow to inspire her next novel.

# Also by Carol MacLean

## The Kiltie Street Girls

*Jeannie's War*
*Elsie's Wartime Wish*

# Elsie's Wartime Wish

## CAROL MacLEAN

**hera**

First published in the United Kingdom in 2023 by

Hera Books
Unit 9 (Canelo), 5th Floor
Cargo Works, 1–2 Hatfields
London SE1 9PG
United Kingdom

A CIP catalogue record for this book is available from the British Library.

Print ISBN 978 1 80436 039 2
Ebook ISBN 978 1 80436 928 9

Look for more great books at www.herabooks.com

Printed and bound in Great Britain by Clays Ltd, Elcograf S.p.A.

I

*For Auntie Ginny*

# Chapter One

'You can't mean it!' Elsie stared in dismay at her mother.

Louise Weir was slumped in the only armchair in their small home.

'I do mean it. I want you to go and fetch Jessie home.'

'But she's so happy and settled with Mr and Mrs Cranston.'

Louise's bleary eyes wavered and blinked before her face tightened and she shook her finger at Elsie. 'She's my wee girl, not theirs. Don't forget that.'

A self-pitying tear rolled down her cheek.

'Of course she's yours. Don't take on so, Ma.'

Elsie slid down onto her knees beside the armchair and stroked her mother's thin arm. A sour smell wafted from the older woman's skin. The gin working its way out of her pores, Elsie thought wearily. Still, she had to be thankful. Ma was usually an affectionate drunk. Although she could be cunning enough with it. Elsie was willing to bet that most of their neighbours were unaware of the problems in the first floor flat at number eight, Kiltie Street. Her mother dressed neatly when she went out and could hold a conversation even after an afternoon tipple or two.

It was, however, getting worse. The bombing over the last couple of years had taken its toll on Louise Weir's nerves and the endless make do and mend, the small weekly rations ever tightening, none of these helped. She'd hardly been a good housekeeper before all that and now, she wasn't coping at all. Truth be told, she had been fond of a tipple for years but the recent incendiary bombing which had damaged Queen's Park church in Govanhill so badly that the building had to be destroyed had shaken her to the core. It wasn't that the church was close to home but she had a friend there whose house was narrowly missed. Elsie also knew that her ma still yearned for the girls' father, even though he had died when the girls were young.

If Elsie wasn't there to make the meals, she wondered how her mother would survive. Especially as she hardly left the flat any more. Maybe that was why she missed Elsie's little sister so much now. Elsie missed Jessie too but there was a war on and that meant making sensible decisions even when they broke your heart. With an eleven-year age gap, Jessie was more like her own child than her wee sister. And Elsie would do anything to make sure she was all right.

'Shall we not just leave Jessie up there in Perthshire where it's safe?' she coaxed gently.

'She's changed. She's got a posh accent now. You weren't there when I went to see her at Christmas. All dressed up... And with a bookcase full of books they've given her.'

'The Cranstons are very kind to her and that's good, isn't it? You don't want her to be without.'

'I don't want her changed, either. She's a Weir, not a Cranston. Give them another while and they'll be wanting to adopt her.'

'I don't think so, Ma. They know she has a loving family here in Glasgow. Surely you don't want to bring her back just yet? Not 'til the war's over and it's safe again.'

'There was a letter…'

'What letter? You never said. What did it say about Jessie?'

Louise waved her arm vaguely but her gaze wouldn't meet Elsie's. Had there been a letter? Elsie couldn't be sure. Her mother was quite capable of a sneaky lie here or there to ease her path to what she wanted.

She stood up, suddenly irritated. 'If there is a letter, I want to see it. Where did you put it?'

Louise shrugged.

'I mean it, Ma. I'm not going unless you give me a good reason to. Show me the letter.'

Her mother struggled upright in the sagging armchair. A wad of stuffing seeped through a rent in the material as she moved and fell to the floor at her feet but she didn't seem to notice. A small smile broke across her face and Elsie was reminded how pretty her mother had once been. She'd often been told she took after her mother in looks, being fair-haired with blue eyes but she didn't have Louise's deep golden curls and almost violet eyes, her colouring being paler. She wondered if she'd inherited that from her father but without any photographs of him in the flat, and with Ma being tight-lipped on the subject, she had no way of telling.

'I'll remember once I've had a nip of the good stuff. Only thing is, I'm out of it.'

3

'There's a war on so I doubt you'll be able to buy any more,' Elsie said, relieved and trying not to show it. Maybe here was a chance to get Ma off the drink, if she'd finally finished her supplies.

'That's where you're wrong. There's a man up the road that I buy from. You take this bag and cash and tell him I sent you.' Louise staggered to her feet and pushed a shopping bag and purse at her. 'Then we'll talk about the letter.'

Elsie wanted to refuse but she bit her lip and took the bag and money. Louise was still her ma and she loved her. Perhaps it wouldn't hurt if she took a little drink and it made her happy. Sometimes she sang songs from her youth and made Elsie dance with her and they laughed as they banged into the furniture in the crowded little room. She liked it when Ma was happy. So much better than the times she found her huddled in the armchair, brows knitted darkly, when she couldn't be roused to interest in anything.

It was a lovely May evening as Elsie walked from Kiltie Street up the hilly road to the large houses with their leafy gardens. Before the war, these houses were well cared for with neatly painted doors and tended hedges and shrubs. She used to enjoy walking past them, glimpsing a different life in the lit windows with their thickly draped curtains pinned back, showing well-off families sitting or eating or reading. She had envied their inhabitants and dreamed of one day living up there herself. It felt like she'd always had to look after Ma and Jessie, as if she was the mother to both of them. Sometimes she wished to be carefree with no ties. She'd seen a girl once, sitting in a window seat up here, gazing out at the view with a book open on her lap, nibbling a biscuit. It had left her with a yearning for an easier life that hadn't gone away.

Before the war she'd been working as a parlour maid at a big house on the south side of the city which hadn't left her much time to dwell on all that. Now she worked at Fearnmore munitions factory which paid much better but here she was at twenty-four, unmarried and still living at home looking after Ma.

Now, the houses at the top of the hill looked as shabby and tired as the tenements lower down the slope. The paint was peeling from doors and the hedges were unkempt where owners were away in the war effort or their gardeners were gone.

The house on the end of the street looked as if it had been neglected well before the war started. The front garden, as small as the others in the row, was full of wild grass so that the path to the front door was hardly visible. The upstairs windows were covered in blackout material even though it was still daylight, as if whoever lived there didn't bother to open the windows at all.

She walked up the path, feeling the grass brush against her legs. She hesitated at the door, then knocked three times just as Ma had instructed. She waited so long that she was turning away when the door opened. She turned back.

'What do you want?'

A man, not much older than herself but with thinning brown hair and a belly that pushed his shirt buttons to the limit, stood there scowling at her.

'I came to buy something,' she said, flustered.

'I don't sell anything. What gave you that idea? This is a private house. Go away.'

Elsie took a step back. She clutched at the bag and felt the hard shape of her mother's purse. That was it; she'd forgotten Ma's instructions. She had to say her name.

He was shutting the door as she blurted out, 'Louise Weir sent me.'

He glanced out quickly in both directions before shepherding her in. 'Don't stand out there, come through here.'

She followed him along a dark hallway which smelt of mildew and towards what might have been a parlour at the back of the house. A wooden counter, like that in a shop, had been fixed across the entrance of the room. He went through the hatch, closing it behind him. Elsie gave him the bag. He didn't seem to need to ask what she wanted.

'Wait here and don't move,' he said.

He disappeared, leaving her in the dank hall. Her shoes felt tacky on the carpet as she moved them. There were cobwebs in the corners of the ceiling as she glanced around. It really felt as if no one lived here.

'Here you are.' He was back. He pushed the bag over to her and she heard the clink of a bottle.

She waited until he led the way back to the front door. Without so much as a nod or a goodbye, he let her out. When she looked back over her shoulder the door was firmly closed.

'What was that all about?' Elsie said, out loud. 'And how did Ma get mixed up in it?'

She felt a rush of affection for Kiltie Street as she turned the corner on the way back. It was a tight-knit community with its row of eight tenement houses, the brickwork stained black by the soot from the local industries. Kiltie Street was part of the Maryhill area and there were plenty of similar rows of tenement housing and the familiar sights, sounds and smells of the chemical works, the ironworks, the rubber factory and more. Nearby was the slowly winding River Kelvin and the busy Forth and Clyde canal and the open fields and woods that edged the great city of Glasgow.

Running up the stone steps to number eight, she let herself into their flat.

'Did you get it?' Louise asked, grabbing for the bag.

'Yes. I think he must've taken the money from your purse. You'd better check he hasn't taken it all.'

Ma shook her head. 'Naw, Archie won't cheat me. We've got a deal, so we have. Just like many others round here. He's no gonnae kill the golden goose, is he now?'

'Shall I make us a pot of tea and we can read the letter together?' Elsie asked.

'You can have tea, I'm going to have a wee nip of this to keep the cold out.' Louise brandished the bottle of gin triumphantly.

Elsie's heart sank. She shouldn't have got it. Although, she thought, if she hadn't, then Ma would likely have gone herself and in her state, the neighbours would have guessed she was the worse for wear.

'Where's the letter?' she persisted.

Louise was busy pouring a generous glass of the clear liquid with an eager smile. She took a large gulp and sighed. She sank down into the armchair and her eyelids lowered.

'Ma?'

A gentle snore rose up and Louise's nostrils quivered. Elsie sighed as she went into the tiny kitchen to make herself a mug of tea.

The journey north to Perthshire took her most of a day. The train was packed with soldiers and the air in the carriage was blue with smoke as men sucked on cigarettes. One soldier with a grizzled, lined face offered her one from his packet of Woodbines. She shook her head and looked away, not wanting the attention. She was squashed into a window seat and someone's kit bag was pinching her toes. She pulled in her legs, trying to make herself even smaller. The train was now in a siding and they'd gone nowhere for what seemed like hours.

With a sigh, Elsie rummaged in her bag and found her jam sandwich. It had to be time for lunch. She didn't own a watch but her stomach was gurgling. She nibbled on the bread to make it last and wondered how Jessie was. She'd missed her dreadfully when they'd decided she ought to be evacuated for a second time after the awful Glasgow blitz in March 1941 but even Ma had agreed Jessie had to be safe and that meant leaving the city. There had been no time to send a letter saying she was coming today. Ma had been firm. Elsie was to go immediately. There was no further mention of the letter she had spoken of before and Elsie had come to realise there was no such thing. Yet all the same, Ma was adamant that she was to go immediately to fetch Jessie home. She missed her wee girl and that was that. It might be a whim but Elsie had to go, Ma was so determined on it.

The train gave a sudden lurch and a cheer went up from the soldiers. A moment later there was a grinding of wheels and a noisy blast of steam and they were moving again. She was simultaneously glad to get going and anxious about getting there. Poor Jessie. What a shock she'd get when Elsie arrived.

The local bus left her in the village square. It was a pretty place with trees coming into leaf. They had paper-white trunks where the bark curled away. There was a flowerbed with sweetpeas in pink and purple and blue. Their scent wafted towards her. The other flowerbeds had lettuce and carrots growing and some other green vegetable she didn't recognise. If she wasn't so nervous, she'd have delighted in it all. As it was, she was too distracted by the thought of Jessie and her reaction to what Elsie had to tell her.

She walked from the square along a lane and out of the village, Ma's directions echoing in her head. Ahead of her and up the hill was thickly wooded. On either side of the woods were fields with cows and sheep. The farmyard sounds were exotic to Elsie's city ears. She pulled her bag closer to her body, feeling exposed in the wide open air. It was all so different from the tenements of Kiltie Street with all their neighbours so close at hand, and the familiar busy, noisy roads in Glasgow. Where was everybody?

Mr and Mrs Cranston lived in a tall house set in its own grounds with the woodlands nestled around it. A breeze ruffled the leaves and made the trees sound as if they were whispering to each other. Elsie glanced up at them and then at the entrance pillars to the property. The path wound round a bend. She followed it and saw the house. It was hard to imagine Jessie living here in this old stone mansion with its tall windows and green shutters and ivy climbing over the doorway. She might as well have been lifted from Kiltie Street and set down on another planet.

An older woman answered the door. Her hair reminded Elsie of the tree bark in the village.

'Mrs Cranston?'

'No dear, I'm Mrs Potter, the Cranstons' housekeeper. What can I do for you?'

'I'm Elsie Weir. I'm here to take my sister home.'

The words came out bluntly despite her practised speech on the walk to the house.

'Oh dear, Mrs Cranston will be so upset. She dotes on that girl. We all do.' Mrs Potter's kindly smile faded.

Elsie was shown into a room to wait while the housekeeper fetched Jessie. She perched uncomfortably on an upright chair and looked about. She was only too aware of her patched summer dress with its faded patterned material and her jacket which she'd made herself from a man's coat bought from a second-hand market. Her shoes were dusty from the walk and she tried not to let them touch the thick carpet.

There was a clatter of feet on the polished tiles outside and Jessie ran towards her, grinning.

'Elsie, is it really you? I didn't know you were coming to visit and I haven't seen you in oh, so long!'

Jessie was different. Elsie hadn't seen her in more than two years and tears blurred her vision as she looked at the bright, healthy girl in front of her. Jessie was taller, nearly as tall as Elsie herself, and her skin glowed. She wasn't the pale, skinny girl who had left Glasgow on a train with her classmates at the beginning of the war, returning briefly only to be sent away again after the city was bombed.

Jessie's black patent shoes tapped impatiently. 'Come on, I want to show you my room. Mrs Potter says I may.'

Ma was right. Jessie's Glasgow accent had softened and there was a Highland lilt to her words.

'I'd like to see your room,' Elsie said.

*I'm here to take you home. I'm here to tear you away from all this.* Those words stuck in her throat unsaid.

Jessie chattered nonstop as they climbed a huge polished wooden stairway and the girl dashed into a room, peeking out to wave Elsie along more quickly. Elsie took a sharp breath in. Jessie's room was big enough to house a small family. A tall window had long embroidered curtains held to the sides with loops of the same cloth. The bed quilt was of eggshell blue which matched the shade of the wallpaper. There was a dressing table and chair and, on one side of the room, a large bookcase full of books.

Elsie went to the window and stared out. The view was of the woods and fields and in the distance was a wide river like a shining band of silver.

'I'm reading *Great Expectations*,' Jessie said, happily, 'Auntie Alison says I'm reading above my age. And Uncle Donald says he's going to buy me *Jane Eyre* when I finish this. They have two boys of their own who are now grown up. Alistair is in the navy and Ronald is in the air force. I'm going to meet them when they come home. See this book, it has pictures, do you want to see it? Elsie?'

Elsie turned, her heart suddenly drumming in her chest. She had to tell Jessie why she was here. But it was difficult. Oh, so difficult. How could she tear her wee sister away from all this?

'Auntie Alison and Uncle Donald – is that Mr and Mrs Cranston, then?' she said, instead.

Jessie nodded. 'That's right. I can't call them Mum and Dad so I call them Auntie and Uncle.'

'You have your own ma,' Elsie said.

'I don't have a dad, though.'

'Our dad's dead, you know that. Anyway, Ma misses you and I do as well.'

Jessie glanced at her and then stared down at her book. 'I miss you both too but I love it here and I love Auntie Alison and Uncle Donald too.'

Elsie knelt on the carpet next to her sister. 'I'm here to take you home. Ma wants you back.'

Jessie turned a page of the book as if reading it. Elsie reached for her hand but Jessie pulled away.

'It's not fair,' she cried, 'I don't want to leave. You can't make me.'

'I'm so sorry. You love Ma, don't you? You don't want to make her sad.'

'I love Ma and I love you,' Jessie said miserably.

'Well then, that's it sorted. I'll go and tell the Cranstons.'

–

The evening meal was a painful affair. Elsie had been introduced to Alison and Donald Cranston by Mrs Potter who explained why she was there. A genteel couple in their sixties, they had remained polite although the anguish on Mrs Cranston's face couldn't be hidden. Mr Cranston said very little except to insist that Elsie stay for the night and that he would drive them to the station in the morning.

After the meal, Jessie went to bed and Elsie was left with two people who were clearly hurting.

'You do realise she is safer here away from Glasgow?' Donald Cranston said.

'My mother wants her home. There's not been bombing since March.'

'We were hoping to adopt Jessie,' Alison Cranston said quietly. 'Would your mother let us do that, do you think?'

So Ma was right. Of course, she'd visited at Christmas and been a couple of times before that. She'd never let Elsie go in her place, always insisting that she was Jessie's ma and that she would go. She must have seen that they were more than fond of Jessie.

Elsie shook her head. 'I'm sorry. Ma won't allow that. She's desperate to have Jessie home again.'

'Then there's no more to be said. Mrs Potter will show you to the guest room. We do hope you are comfortable there. I won't be at breakfast so I'll say goodbye now.'

Alison Cranston rose from the sofa and Elsie realised she was being dismissed. Awkwardly, she got up too. The Cranstons were right. There really was no more to be said. They were suffering and Jessie was, too. At that moment, Elsie cursed her mother for her drunken whims. If the Germans came back to bomb Glasgow again and something terrible happened, she would never forgive herself for giving in to Ma's orders.

Donald Cranston drove them to the station the next morning after breakfast, Elsie wondering silently how he managed to get a petrol permit. Jessie didn't say anything but hugged him until Elsie gently took her arm and pulled her away.

'Remember to write to us,' he said. 'Be a good girl for your mother and if you need us, you know where we are. Here, this is for you.'

He gave Jessie a small package before getting into his car. Elsie was glad to see the train arrive in a blast of hot steam and she hurried Jessie along the platform. The journey back to Glasgow was just as long and tiring as the journey out had been. Jessie refused to talk, pressing her nose to the window and staring out. She shook her head when Elsie offered her sandwiches that Mrs Potter had made up for them.

–

Elsie had hoped that when Jessie saw Kiltie Street again, she'd be excited to be home. But her sister walked slowly, scuffing her shiny patent leather shoes until Elsie wanted to scream at her. She bit her lip. Of course it was difficult. Jessie had been away for over two years. There had to be an adjustment. Opening the door to their small flat, she smelled cabbage and coal tar soap.

'Come on, Jessie, don't just stand there.'

Jessie's lower lip trembled. Elsie shook her head and went in. Louise appeared, stumbling from the parlour.

'Where is she, my wee darling?' she slurred, pushing past Elsie.

Jessie recoiled as Louise draped her arms around her and held her tightly. Then she seemed to fold into her mother as if resigned to being back. The powerful smell of cabbage emanated from the kitchen as Elsie went in to put the kettle on the range for tea. Dirty dishes sat in the sink and the overhead pulley of laundry hadn't been touched since she left. The curtain across the recess bed where Louise slept hung open and the grimy bedclothes were visible. All at once, the dirt and disorder of their home was as clear as if she were a visitor glimpsing it for the first time, and she was ashamed when she thought of the contrast to the beautiful home the Cranstons lived in. Ma wasn't coping. That was obvious.

'Cup of tea?' she called through, trying for a cheerful tone and thinking of Jessie and how she must be feeling.

'Aye, darling, bring a pot for the three of us. Jessie, get your coat off, you're home now, and help Elsie with the cups.'

They sat in the parlour. It was grandly named for what it was. There was a wooden table and three chairs, a sideboard which Louise had bought years before, the fireplace and a wireless. A brown curtain, tatty with age, hung over the second recess bed, hiding the space which Elsie considered her own.

Louise's hands shook as she took a cup of tea.

'Are you all right, Ma?'

'Aye, a wee bit under the weather, so I am, but I'm fine. I've no' been back to Archie's if that's what you mean.'

Elsie saw with concern that Ma's eyes had a creamy-yellow cast to them. That didn't seem normal. She was wincing too, as if her belly hurt. Just as she took a sip of tea, Louise gave out a cry and dropped the cup. Her whole body shook and beads of sweat popped out on her grey skin.

'Ma!' Jessie screamed.

'Jessie, run for Dr Graham,' Elsie said, pushing the tray of tea away and rushing to Louise.

'Don't be daft. We cannae afford the doctor,' Louise puffed, staring at Elsie with terrified eyes.

'Yes, we can,' Jessie said.

She stuck out her hand and Elsie saw the package that Mr Cranston had given her. Jessie had torn it open and there were coins within.

'Go now,' Elsie urged her.

Jessie scampered away, the package left on the table filling Elsie with guilt. Not only had they dragged her sister away from a happy, safe home, now she had to give up her gift of money to help them.

Louise moaned and went rigid. In terror, Elsie saw foam gather at the corners of her mother's mouth and she no longer seemed to notice that anyone was there. She ran through to the kitchen and grabbed the blanket from Ma's bed and put it over her. There was nothing else to be done but wait for the doctor and to pray for Ma's life.

When the fit was done, Ma slept. She was deep in muscle-twitching dreams when Dr Graham arrived. He gave her a thorough examination while Elsie and Jessie waited in the kitchen. Elsie kept Jessie busy chopping carrots for their tea while she boiled potatoes. There was very little else to eat in the house. Ma hadn't been shopping. She relied on Elsie to do that. Now the shops were shut for the day so the vegetables would have to fill them up. There was a loaf of National Bread, grey and dry, in the bread tin. She'd put a drop of water on a few slices and heat them up.

'Your mother's comfortable now.' Doctor Graham put his head round the door.

Elsie went out into the small hallway. 'Thank you, Doctor, for coming. What's wrong with her?'

The doctor shook his greying head. He knew all the inhabitants of Kiltie Street and had been the family doctor for years. Not that they called him often. It was expensive and most folk went to one of the local women who offered home cures for a little money or a few veg or whatever people could afford.

'I don't want to upset you, my dear, but I must speak plainly. Your mother's body has become used to drink and it would seem she hasn't been drinking for a few days. She's had a small fit from the withdrawal.'

'And is she all right now? Is she well again?'

'I've given her something for her discomfort. She has pain in her midriff which concerns me and she's jaundiced. She may need to come into hospital but let's see what we can do in the meantime. I'll come and visit again tomorrow.'

Elsie didn't like to say that she couldn't afford that. She prayed that Donald Cranston's gift would cover it. Somehow she'd pay Jessie back the money.

'Thank you, Doctor.'

He turned back at the door. 'If she is coming off the drink it must be for the love of her two daughters. You should be glad of that. She has to do it gradually, though. You must monitor her. I'll see you tomorrow.' He tipped his hat to her politely.

Ma slept on. In the end, they slipped a pillow under her head on the armchair, tucked her blanket in and left her there. Elsie and Jessie climbed up into the recess bed and drew the curtain over. They snuggled in together and Elsie was glad of Jessie's warm body against hers.

'I'm still hungry,' Jessie murmured.

'I'm sorry about that. We'll have a good tea tomorrow once I've got in the shopping.'

Elsie kissed her sister's hair and held her close. Whatever happened, she vowed to herself fiercely, whatever it took, she'd keep Jessie safe.

## Chapter Two

'One more push, Annie, one big push now!'

Annie screamed and the blockage between her legs shifted and moved in a rush of hot liquid. Her hair was wet with sweat and she smelled the metallic odour of fresh blood. Cramps rippled through her body and she cried out again as a final push expelled the afterbirth.

'It's a boy. You've got a beautiful baby boy.' Mrs Wiley's smiling face loomed over her and Annie sank back on the pillows. 'Now, let's get him latched on to feed and we'll get you tidied up for your husband.'

Annie stared in wonder at the tiny being in her arms. Mrs Wiley pushed down her unbuttoned nightie and pressed the baby's face to Annie's large, brown nipple. It was disturbing, the changes pregnancy had made to her body. She hadn't enjoyed it one little bit but it was worth it now she saw him. Her baby. Her very own. He made a small mewling sound like a kitten and turned his damp head, still streaked with blood, away from her breast.

'Why won't he take it?' she said.

'He will. Give him a moment. He'll root soon enough. Now, what are you naming him?'

'Davey. David Paul Thom.' Paul had chosen the name but Annie was happy with it.

'A good strong name for a boy. That's you all freshened up and if you shift a wee bit, I'll slip this clean sheet under you. That's it.'

The baby's hard gums latched onto Annie's tender nipple and she cried out. She felt as if she'd done nothing but cry for the last nine months, what with one thing and another.

'There you are. He's feeding nicely now. You'll learn together to be Mum and baby. It's not all instinct. But your mother will help you. Is she staying?'

Annie nodded, her gaze not leaving Davey. 'She's staying for the week to help.'

Mrs Wiley smiled as if Annie had passed some test. 'That's good. I'll go and bring Mr Thom in to meet his son.'

Annie felt herself tense as she sat, propped up on the pillows, Davey attached like a leech to her chest. She pulled her nightie up round him primly. Paul came in.

'A son, then?' he said gruffly.

She nodded. He leaned over and kissed her cheek, laying a large hand on Davey's soft head. She glanced up and saw tears in his eyes. Suddenly he was the Paul she had married less than a year ago and before their troubles had started.

'Will you hold him?' she said, pulling Davey gently away from her body and ready to offer him to his father.

'How can I?' Paul moved away and there was a bitter twist to his mouth. 'I've only one arm, it's not possible.'

She looked at his pinned-up sleeve on his left arm where the limb was missing from just below the elbow. *Half an arm, Paul. You're missing half an arm and there's plenty of others who didn't come home at all. Can't you be happy at that?*

'I'm sorry,' she mumbled. 'I never thought…'

He sighed, letting the sound whistle accusingly between them. Davey flexed his tiny body suddenly and she tightened her grip on him. What if she let him fall? He let out a wailing cry that didn't stop.

'What should I do?' she said, rocking him to and fro and feeling desperate.

'I'll send Mrs Wiley,' Paul said and slipped from the room.

The midwife bustled back in a few minutes later along with Annie's mother. Ivy Morris was a stout woman with thick, black hair as luxuriant as Annie's and bristling black eyebrows that had signalled all Annie's life as to whether her mother was pleased or otherwise. Now those bushy eyebrows were raised in anticipation of seeing her first and only grandchild.

Ivy had been an invalid for the past few years – *when it suited her*, Annie couldn't help think – but the birth of her first grandchild seemed to have galvanised her into getting up from her bed and coming up to the city to look after him.

Ivy pushed past Mrs Wiley to get to the bedside first.

'Give him here. I'll soothe him. Who's a bonny boy, then?' she crooned, almost snatching Davey from Annie's clasp.

Mrs Wiley gave Annie a cheeky wink behind Ivy's back.

'Here, Mrs Morris. Sit yourself down here on this chair and take the weight off. That'll be better for baby.'

The eyebrows twitched at the mention of taking the weight off but Ivy did as she was told and sat and rocked Davey until he quietened. She looked over at Annie.

'That's how it's done. You mustn't give in to them and coddle them, of course. Spare the rod and spoil the child.'

'He's a newborn baby, Mum.'

'Aye, well, they all have to learn.' She paused, inspecting Davey. 'He's the spit of Brian at that age, so he is.'

'He looks like Paul with that dark hair,' Annie said.

Ivy pursed her lips. 'Perhaps.'

'Give him back now, Mum, I'll feed him again.'

Annie stretched out her arms for her son. For an awful moment she thought Ivy was going to refuse. But she struggled out of the chair, complaining of sore knees, and gave Davey back.

'Where is Paul? He should be in here as the proud father,' Ivy said, disapprovingly.

'He... he can't hold Davey and he got upset.'

Ivy snorted. 'He needs to pull himself together and be the man of the house. How long is he going to mope around before he gets a job and supports you? It's been five months since he was invalided out of the army and he's done nothing in all that while.'

Although her mother's sharp words echoed Annie's own thoughts at times, she wasn't going to agree with her. That would only fuel the dislike that simmered between her mum and Paul.

'He's got his pension now he's out of the army. We'll manage on that.'

'Well, you can hardly go back to work at the munitions. Not for a while, at any rate. Lucky for you I can stay here for a week to help. Not longer, mind. Just in case Brian comes home.'

Annie bit her lip. No matter how many times she told her, Ivy refused to believe that her brother Brian wasn't coming home for at least five years or more. He'd been caught as a deserter during the Clydebank blitz when their home was bombed. Ivy had been sheltering and feeding him for months until he was discovered. He was currently serving a five-year prison sentence and, if the war still raged when he got out, there was no doubt he'd be sent back to the army.

'He's not coming home for a while,' she said, trying anyway.

'Anyone would think you didn't want your brother to come back.'

'That's not true. I miss him just as much as you do. I stayed up plenty of nights to make him meals when he was hiding out.'

The exhaustion she felt now echoed those months when Brian had hidden up in the hills during the days and sneaked down to their house after dark for food and shelter.

'Here, give me my grandson. You should take a nap.'

---

'You're so clever,' Jeannie said when she came to visit Annie a few days later. 'He's gorgeous, so he is. Aren't you, wee man?'

She rocked Davey gently as she paced the bedroom. Not that there was much space, what with the iron bedstead, the dresser and now Davey's cot. Annie liked to call it a cot even though it was the dresser's bottom drawer, lined with clean newspapers and one of her old nightdresses. They couldn't afford a proper cot. When she was pregnant she'd seen one in Lewis's, the grand department store in the city centre, and dreamed of owning it.

'You're a dab hand at that,' Annie remarked, glad to hand the baby over and take a little rest.

'I've had plenty of practice with Dennis,' Jeannie said. 'Mum often lets me and Kathy look after him when she gets tired. Oh, that reminds me, that parcel there is a wee gift from all of us.'

Annie took the parcel, wrapped in brown paper and string, and opened it slowly, taking care not to tear the paper. She put the string aside and folded the paper so that she could give it back to Jeannie.

'They're lovely, thanks.' She lifted the tiny garments and stroked them.

'They're not new I'm afraid but they're in good condition. I can't believe Dennis was so tiny he could fit into them. You should see him now.'

'What is he, eighteen months?' Annie asked politely.

There had been some gossip at the time what with Jeannie's younger sister, Kathy, being suddenly evacuated and Jeannie's mother, Mary, surprising everyone by getting married again to her neighbour, Harry. Dennis had arrived early, or so the story went, and there were some who were certain that Kathy was the baby's mother. Annie didn't want to ask. It was Jeannie's family's affair, after all.

'That's right, eighteen months and a big bruiser. Take it from me, enjoy it now while Davey can't walk. Once he's on his feet you'll have no peace. So, you settled in here all right?'

Annie nodded. 'It was good of you to tell us about the flat for rent. Paul was keen for us to get a place of our own.'

'It must be hard having the baby only a couple of weeks after you moved in.'

'You can see for yourself; we're all at sixes and sevens,' Annie sighed.

'Still, you've got your mum to help.'

Annie opened her mouth and shut it again. She couldn't tell Jeannie the truth. That she wished her mother would go home to Dumbarton. The flat wasn't big enough for all of them and Ivy took up more than her fair share of space.

She changed the subject. 'How's Eileen?'

She, Jeannie and Eileen had all started the same day at the local munitions factory and become friends.

'She's fine, I think. I haven't had a letter this week. She's enjoying living in Devon and her cottage sounds pretty. Mind, the factory work and hours sound the same as up here.'

'It's awful far away from Glasgow.'

'It is but she thinks if Jimmy gets leave he can make it back there easier than getting up to Scotland.'

'She's hopeful,' Annie said drily. 'Are they not all fighting in Africa now?'

Jeannie shrugged. She handed Davey back to Annie and sat next to her on the bed.

'I don't know. My Bill's away down south as well. I'd maybe join Eileen but I can't leave Mum and Kathy and Dennis. I'd even miss Harry, come to that. He's more like a real dad than my stepdad.'

'What's happening at Fearnmore?' Annie felt an unexpected pang when she asked. She hadn't much enjoyed working there but now she sort of wished she could.

'Not much. Just the same noisy old machines and the endless shell casings. I was a bit lonely, what with you and Eileen gone, but I've got friendlier with Ruby and her pals, Letty and Barbara, so it's not so bad now.'

'What about that girl you get the bus with?'

'Elspeth Weir? Elsie's all right but Jimmy's never liked her so it makes it a wee bit uncomfortable being too friendly, you know? Jimmy might be my big, annoying brother but we're close, so it matters.'

Davey began to cry. Annie unbuttoned her shirt and guided his mouth to her breast. She still found it awkward and all she could smell was her own milk. It reeked from her skin no matter how often she washed.

'You're so lucky,' Jeannie said, twisting her wedding ring on her finger. 'I'd love to have a baby but it hasn't happened yet. And now Bill's away so no chance until he gets leave.'

Annie didn't know what to say. She concentrated on baby Davey's head and the way his little hands curled and uncurled as he suckled. She and Jeannie were friends but she'd always felt... extra... as Jeannie and Eileen were clearly best friends. There had been times when their heads were bent together, their stifled giggling indicated some shared joke and she'd hated them for leaving her out of it.

Jeannie gave a loud yawn and clapped her hand over her mouth.

'Pardon me, but I'm that tired from working. The shifts are so long these days. I'd better get going. I'm up again at six tomorrow and the girls have roped me into going to a dance in the evening.'

Annie waved her off at the flat door and felt unsettled after she'd gone. Jeannie's life, it seemed, was going along nicely. She still had her job and now her new friends and enough energy to go dancing. While Annie was stuck in her flat with a demanding baby needing to be fed at all hours, a husband who couldn't help much, and Ivy.

She went into the kitchen, intending to make a cup of tea. Loud reverberating snores came from the recess bed. The curtain was closed. Ivy was asleep. Paul was sitting in the armchair with the wireless playing.

'We used to dance to that tune.' Annie smiled.

Paul grunted but didn't look up.

'Do you want to hold him?' she asked. 'I can prop him up on your good arm.'

'Leave it, will you,' Paul said, sharply.

She flinched and felt ready tears pricking the backs of her eyelids. She kissed Davey's soft head and smelled the sweet, milky warmth of him. She didn't mind the milk smell on him.

Paul stood up. 'I'm away out.'

'Where are you going?'

'The pub,' he said shortly, not meeting her gaze.

'Don't go,' she said. 'Stay in with me and Davey. We can listen to music.'

'I've listened to enough music tonight while Jeannie was here.'

'We can't afford it,' Annie said quickly, 'if you're drinking. It's dear and we're not working, either of us.'

'You've become a real nag and I'm not staying here to be nagged at. Don't wait up,' Paul snapped.

He slammed the door on his way out, making her jump and Davey cry. She hushed him, not caring that her tears were splashing onto his face. She sat on Paul's vacated armchair with her baby and thought back to when she'd first met him. It had been at Janet's wedding. Janet had proudly introduced her oldest brother and Annie was immediately drawn to his dark good looks and cheeky humour. He was charming and happy-go-lucky, as if he had no cares in the world. He made her laugh and forget the weary secret of hiding Brian.

Even more surprisingly, he had been attracted to her too. Annie knew her best features were her long, black glossy hair and clear skin. She wasn't slender like Jeannie or vivacious like Eileen. She was plump and bulky and she took after Ivy in shape but Paul had flirted with her and asked her out and they had fallen in love.

Even Janet's death in the Clydebank blitz hadn't changed him completely. It had left him angry and determined to fight the Nazis but still loving towards her. They got married just before he left for overseas duty and their wedding day was full of love and tenderness and happiness. Annie was pregnant before he left. And then, all too quickly, he was home again. Invalided out of the army with his forearm blown off. It was as if a different man had come home.

'Will I ever see my lovely Paul again?' Annie whispered to Davey.

—

'Where's your purse? I'm away to get the messages,' Ivy shouted the next morning.

'Mum, keep your voice down, Paul's asleep,' Annie hissed.

'Asleep at this hour? He should be ashamed of himself. Most men are up and at work hours ago. It's as I warned you before you got married. I could tell. He's all charm and no substance, that one.'

'Will you get a scrag end of lamb for tea? We're out of milk and we could do with some carrots,' Annie said, deciding to ignore Ivy's snide remarks.

'I'll try. Goodness knows what I'll find in the shops. I join one queue and by the time I reach the end, whatever it was has gone.'

'Just get what you can, then. We can make a meal out of it somehow.'

'Your purse? I've got the ration cards.'

Annie went to get her purse from the bedroom but opening it, she saw it was empty of coins. She glared at Paul's back where he lay, a covered lump, under the blanket. So that was how he had afforded his trip to the pub. She went back out to the small hallway where Ivy was tapping her foot, the eyebrows pinched together, letting Annie know how slow she was being.

'Well?'

'I… can you lend us some, please? I'm a bit low on cash.'

'I see. It's himself, isn't it? Blown it on watered-down beer, no doubt.'

'I'm sorry, I know it's a lot to ask what with you helping me out with the baby and being out of your own home this week…' Annie trailed off helplessly.

Honestly, if Ivy didn't help out, she didn't know what she was going to do. And her mother was quite capable of saying no, if she thought it was the right thing to do.

Ivy gave a loud sigh and delved into her large handbag. It was shiny with age and Annie had never known her mum to have another one. She rummaged about and then nodded, bringing out her own purse and checking its contents.

'Never let it be said that Ivy Morris would let her family go hungry. Not even her useless son-in-law. For Davey's sake, I'll pay for your shopping.'

'Thanks, Mum. I'll pay you back.'

She had no idea how. Paul's army pension was small and it was hard to live on it even without a baby to feed. She decided to worry about that later. It was how she coped these days. One worry at a time.

When Ivy had gone, mumbling under her breath, Annie sank down onto the kitchen chair to feed Davey. Her breasts felt hot and tender and she cried out as he latched on. Afterwards, she tiptoed into the bedroom and put him in his makeshift cot for a nap. Feeling a headache coming on, she went back into the kitchen to sit.

When Ivy came back, Annie was still sitting at the kitchen table, her head in her hands.

'What's the matter with you?' Ivy asked, putting her laden bags onto the table and making Annie's head thump painfully.

'I don't feel well. My head's sore and my chest feels hot and tight.'

'Let me see.'

Ivy was already tugging at her blouse, loosening it. Annie was embarrassed but Ivy shook her head.

'I've seen it all before. I gave birth to you, didn't I? Your skin's all shiny. Hot too, is it?'

Annie nodded. 'What's wrong with me?'

'Nothing that a few cabbage leaves won't sort out. Lucky for you, there was no carrots to be had so I bartered a couple of sausages with your neighbour up the road for a cabbage.'

'Sausages for a cabbage? I don't think that you got the best end of the bargain,' Annie said, rubbing her chest gently and feeling the heat sear through her thin blouse and into her fingertips.

Ivy snorted. 'That's because you didn't see the quality of the sausages. They're all bread and rubbish. I'd be surprised if they'd ever seen a pig in their life.'

She peeled the outer leaves off the cabbage and put them aside. Then, to Annie's surprise, she got the rolling pin and began to crush some of the inner, fresh green leaves on the table top.

'Now, slip a leaf into each bra cup and that'll cool your skin down and stop the swelling.'

'Are you joking?'

'I'm serious. Now do what you're told.'

Ivy's tone brooked no argument. Annie rolled her eyes but slipped the cabbage leaves into place and straightened her clothes.

'I used the same cure myself after I had you. You were a sickly baby.'

'I didn't know that.'

'Why would you? I had no bother with Brian; he was always a healthy wee boy but you… oh, you tried me sorely, I tell you.'

Annie repressed the urge to roll her eyes again. Of course Brian would've been perfect. At least in Ivy's view.

'Thanks, Mum, for the cabbage leaves.'

Ivy pressed in her chins and waved her away but Annie could see she was pleased.

'All right, I'm going up the road now for a cuppa with Mrs Lennox at number five. I met her yesterday and we had a right good blether. She said to look in on her and that's what I'm going to do.'

–

An hour later, Annie was steeping nappies in two buckets while Davey wriggled on a blanket on the floor beside her. She wrinkled her nose over the stink. Even the open kitchen window didn't make a difference. The crash of a door made Davey startle, his eyes round and his limbs flailing. He opened his pink mouth and wailed.

Paul staggered into the kitchen. His hair was flattened on one side and his face creased from sleep. There were pouches under his eyes. He recoiled at the smell of nappies and filthy water.

'Bloody hell, what are you cooking up?'

'I'm washing Davey's towels.'

'They stink. And will you shut him up? I've got the mother of all headaches.' He clutched at his head and groaned.

'He's only a baby. That's what they do, they cry.'

'Shut him up! If you won't then I'll do it,' Paul shouted.

His face was suffused with dark red and, for a moment, Annie thought him quite ugly. With a sob, she swept the howling baby up in her arms and pushed past her husband, reaching the safety of the bedroom. Davey was hot and restless and oh, so loud. The sounds shrieked in her ears. She knew she ought to soothe him but suddenly it was all too much. She put him down into his cot drawer where he thrashed about.

Annie sat on the edge of the bed. Outside the bedroom, in the rest of their small home, was an angry, resentful man. A man she wasn't sure still loved her. The cabbage leaves rustled and tugged at her painful skin. Her hair was greasy and her face had come out in spots because she hadn't washed it for days. She pressed the palms of her hands over her ears and stared at the baby in the drawer. The newspaper was visible over the rumpled material of her old nightie surrounding him. Davey's face was puce. She ought to do something. Instead, she wished she'd never had a baby at all.

# Chapter Three

Doris pushed her thick-lensed spectacles onto the top of her head. She might not be able to see very far without them but close up, the newspaper print was wonderfully clear. Her mousey brown hair fell across her cheeks and she pushed it back behind her ears.

'I don't know why you bother with all that. It'll give you nightmares,' her mother said, bustling about in the tiny kitchen, hanging pots below the shelf and reaching for a polishing rag to shine the range.

'I like to know what's going on,' Doris said, reading the front page for the second time. 'The headline is "*Zero Hour Approaching. Lampedusa points way to big events.*" I wonder what that means?'

Leila Connelly paused in her rubbing of the range. 'I really don't want to know.'

Doris didn't hear her. She frowned and rubbed the bridge of her nose where her spectacles had left a dent like an angry scar.

'Ah, here it is. Further down it says that Mr Churchill announces *amphibious operations on a large scale – Allies resolute plan to strike soon against Hitler's European Fortress.* What does "amphibious" mean? Oooh, there's a map an' all, showing Lampedusa, Tunisia and Malta. It's an island. Fancy that.'

'Well, if you won't have nightmares, I will. I'd rather keep my wee home clean and bright and think about something nice.'

'Where's Dad's dictionary, Mum?'

Leila sighed. 'It's in the kist under my bed. I put it back there when you stopped using it so much.'

'I did use it a lot, didn't I? I'm quite proud of myself, I know a lot of meanings of things now.'

'Where's it going to take you? There's no point bettering yourself above your station.'

'I'm not trying to be uppity, Mum. I like knowing things. That's all.'

'You've got a good job. I don't want you throwing all that away on a daydream.'

'I'm not,' Doris insisted.

She went to get the dictionary. It was battered with age but she loved it because it had her dad's signature on the flyleaf. His hand was bold and the letters were copperplate, flowery and dramatic. She liked to imagine that he had been bold and dramatic too. But she had no idea. He had died when she was two and her mum didn't talk about him. All she knew was that she took after him in her love of book learning. And that was a comfort. She felt close to him as she sifted through the delicate, thin pages searching for 'amphibious'.

'It means able to live both on land and in the water as frogs and toads. Mmm, that can't be what Mr Churchill means, surely. No, here it is – "*relating to military forces and equipment organised for operations launched from the sea against an enemy shore*",' she said to herself.

Doris shivered. It was one thing to read it in a dictionary but quite another to imagine all those poor soldiers in their boats reaching the shores of an island where Hitler's forces were waiting for them. How awful it must be. How frightened they would be. She put the dictionary back in the carved, wooden kist and pushed it back into its place in the alcove under the bed recess. They had a small home and everything had a particular place in order to keep it tidy.

'When are you heading out again?' Leila asked, twisting the cuffs of her housecoat.

'I'll catch the bus at half four as usual. The shifts at Fearnmore might change and I heard the girls grumbling about longer hours but they still want the cleaners in regular as clockwork.'

'You've got time to go into the back court for me then and water my plants.'

'I thought you like to do that? You love your garden.'

Leila left off worrying her cuffs and pressed a shaky hand up to her chest.

'What's the matter, Mum? Is it that Mr Gibb again from across the way?'

Doris watched in concern as her mother sank down onto a kitchen chair, trembling.

'He keeps scowling at me,' she said. 'I'm scared to go into the garden at all, now.'

'Och, Mum, he doesn't mean anything by it, I'm sure. He's probably lonely, living all by himself.'

'All the same, I'd rather not see him. Will you go? But take care. Don't look at him, just pretend you don't see him. And hurry back. Here's the watering can. You'll need to water all the veg on the Andie and in the wee strip on the grass.'

Doris dutifully filled the metal watering can from the tap and lugged it down the stone steps at the back entrance to the tenement. Thank goodness they lived in the ground floor flat. She liked living in Kiltie Street and their home was right at the end at number one where the row was close to another tenement block so it was lively with families. She liked seeing the children playing out, even though nowadays there were fewer of them, what with so many being evacuated and not coming home. Nowadays, the children played in the bomb craters and collected pieces of shrapnel as prizes. Willowherb sprouted in the craters, not quite in flower but almost ready to burst into its bright pink splendour. There was so much of it in the bombed areas at the Singer factory in Clydebank that it was now known locally as 'Singer weed'.

Her heart began to thud as she put her foot down off the last stone step into the back court. The mounded top of the Anderson shelter took up most of the space. Before the war they'd been lucky to have a grass lawn instead of concrete. Now it was all dug up and made into slightly haphazard rows of vegetables and a little plot of colourful flowers, while a few dandelions and plantains increased the variety. At least on the Connellys' side of the line. On Mr Gibb's side it was regimented rows of vegetables, in strict order with not a weed to be seen.

Doris tried hard to keep her worries to herself. Her mum wasn't strong and was prone to feeling anxious. The trouble was, her fear was infectious. And right now, Doris was terrified of meeting Mr Gibb. The thick bottle glass of her lenses prevented her seeing all round and she felt her breath catch. *Oh please, no.* Please God, don't let me have an asthma attack right now, she thought. Breathe in and out. Slowly, mind. Just the way Dr Graham had shown her when she was a child.

She hurried with the heavy watering can, spilling water onto her feet in her rush to get the plants done. She splattered them, watching the soil darken. She turned to go back into the tenement and gasped. Mr Gibb was standing there, staring at her. He was blocking her path.

'Excuse me,' she whispered, bringing the empty watering can to her chest as if it could protect her.

He moved towards her and Doris's heart gave a painful lurch. Then he turned in towards his own patch of ground and she saw he was holding a garden hoe. He pushed it along the soil, ignoring her. Doris ran up the steps and back into the house. Once inside, she leant against the door. It was cool against her back. She took a raspy breath.

'Did you see him?' Leila said.

'No,' Doris lied.

'I'm glad you're here, love. I don't know what I'd do without you. I'm glad you couldn't join up. It's a blessing. That's what it is. I need you here.'

–

Her asthma attack came the next morning in the shop. She was fetching Franny's morning cup of tea.

'Black and no sugar, as there isn't any,' Franny shouted into the back room. 'If I ever catch that Hitler, he'll know all about it. Fancy not being able to have sugar in your tea. I can hardly remember my tea with three spoonfuls before rationing.'

Doris didn't need to be told. Franny said the same thing every morning. She put the battered kettle on and reached for the tea caddy. All at once, she felt it. Her breath laboured and she wheezed. She sucked in air. Her chest rattled and she couldn't get enough of it.

'Where's that tea?' Franny popped her head in, her black bombazine dress rustling. 'Oh, heavens, are you having an attack? Sit down, girl. That's it. Leave the bloomin' tea leaves and calm yourself. In, out, breathe.'

Doris tried to breathe. It was like taking air in through a narrow straw. She mustn't panic. Dr Graham always said panic would make it worse. And he was right. So now she concentrated on calming herself. But oh, it was hard because it was scary. Gradually, her breath slowed.

'That's better,' Franny said, 'You've got a bit of colour back in your cheeks. Now, what brought that on?'

'Must be the dust,' Doris said, her voice thin and reedy.

'Dust. What a cheek. There's no dust in here. Or, if there is, it's your fault as it's your job to do the dusting.' Franny thrust a cup of tea under her nose. 'Here, drink that up. I've put an extra few leaves into it. Goodness knows, I'll regret it tomorrow when we've none.'

Doris sipped the hot tea gratefully. 'I'll be all right now and I can serve at the counter in a moment.'

Franny sighed. 'I should get another girl in to help but they're all away in the forces or the munitions factories. Lucky for me that you failed your medical.'

Doris bit her lip on an answer. Franny shook her head, muttering, and went back out into the shop. The morning went on much as usual. Franny's regulars came in for a variety of objects but some left empty-handed. Her boast was that Franny's Emporium had everything anyone needed but these days there were plenty of empty shelves and the window display was sparse. There was a complaint about the dreary cream and brown pottery on show and, although Doris explained that they were only allowed to sell plain pottery as the government had banned the manufacture of decorated versions, this didn't go down well with the customer. As for rubber boots – why anyone even asked was a puzzle. Of course there were none.

Doris was thinking about Roy when she broke the jug. She had the feather duster and was lightly brushing it over the shelves but in her mind she was looking forward to discussing the latest news with him. Unfortunately, her elbow knocked the jug as she went past and it went sailing off the shelf to crash to the floor.

It smashed with an echoing noise. A customer, chatting to Franny, jumped and screamed. Franny's eyes bulged in surprise.

'I'm so sorry, Mrs Miller. My shop assistant has had a little accident. Have a seat while you recover your nerves. Doris, what is going on?'

'I… I've broken a jug. I'm awfully sorry.'

'You're costing me a fortune. It's not the first mishap, is it?'

'It's my specs. I don't see too good even with them. I'm really short-sighted.'

'You don't say.'

'You can take it off my wages,' Doris said miserably.

'Aye, well, we can discuss that later. Clear it up now, will you. We don't want Mrs Miller or the other customers cutting their feet on it.'

Doris knelt down and picked up the shards. The jug wasn't shattered, exactly. A couple of big pieces had come off it. She had a sudden idea.

'I can fix it, I think. You could sell it for cheaper and then it wouldn't be wasted,' she said eagerly.

Franny looked at her. 'Have a go, if you like. I won't be annoyed if you don't manage it.'

'Thank you. I promise I'll bring it back good as new – or almost, at any rate.'

Franny mumbled something that Doris couldn't quite hear. She didn't care, though. She carefully put the china pieces into her cloth bag. She was absolutely certain that Roy could fix it. He was a dab hand at that sort of thing.

Franny's Emporium shut at five p.m. but Doris finished up in the shop every day at two. Franny said she could manage those hours on her own, and it meant Doris had time to get ready for her next job at Fearnmore munitions factory. Wednesday was Franny's half-day closing and Doris dreaded it. Her Wednesday afternoon was spent at her worst job. Anyway, she wasn't going to worry about that just now. She hurried along the pavement, cradling her bag with the broken jug in her arms. It would be just like her to trip on a paving slab and break the rest of it.

She knocked on the door of the ground floor flat at number two Kiltie Street where the Allen family lived in a single room – known in Glasgow as a 'single end'. Doris knew she and her mum were poor but they were well off compared to the Allens.

Roy opened the door and grinned when he saw her. Doris's heart fluttered in her chest. With his dark brown hair and sea-blue eyes, Roy Allen was gorgeous. When he grinned, a dimple appeared on his right cheek. It made her want to reach out and touch it.

'Hello, how's my girl?' Roy said, holding the door open for her.

If only she were his girl. But she knew he was just being nice. That was Roy, always cheerful and kind to everyone.

'I'm fine, thanks. I didn't get you up, did I?' she asked, anxiously.

'No, you're all right. I can't sleep much after midday. Too noisy by half in here.'

'I don't know how you can do night shifts. I like to get up in the morning and go to bed after dark.'

'Och, you get used to it.'

Roy's yawn and rub of the eyes told a different story but he wasn't one to complain, Doris knew that.

'Hello, Mr Allen,' she said to the old man, sitting in the wooden rocking chair by the range.

He had a tartan blanket over his knees in spite of the stuffy warmth of the room. He smiled kindly at her.

'That you, young Doris? Come to see our Roy again, have you? You're here so often, I thought you'd moved in.'

'That's enough, Grandad. Don't tease her. You know we love Doris's visits.'

Doris felt the heat rising in her cheeks as Roy's grandad winked behind Roy's back. He was a bit of a joker but sometimes his teasing was too close to the bone.

'You're lucky,' Roy went on, picking up a pile of fresh washing so that Doris could sit on a kitchen chair, 'Ma's out serving in the canteen and the kids are at school so we've got peace, apart from Grandad.'

'Bring me a pillow for ma heid and I'll be no bother,' Jock Allen said with another wink.

Roy gave a dramatic sigh. 'No bother, that'll be right. One pillow coming up.'

'I'll get it,' Doris said.

It wasn't as if there was far to go to get it. How nine people lived their lives in this one small room was beyond her imagination. Roy's dad was on the convoys and two of his sisters lived out while they worked at the Royal Ordnance Factory in Bishopton but even so, it had to be a squeeze for the rest of them. There was the usual recess bed hidden by a curtain in the wall, a hurley bed on casters underneath, and two mattresses were propped on their sides to the wall so that the rest of the family slept on the floor each night with some comfort.

A pulley of damp washing hung on the kitchen ceiling over the range. Above the range was the traditional shelf with hooks underneath where pots and utensils hung. They might have very little space but Roy's mum kept everything spotless. There was a press, too, and the space where the coal was kept. These were familiar to Doris as the layouts of the tenement flats weren't ever too different but if you were lucky, you had more than one room to call your own.

She busied herself pulling a pillowcase from a pile of fresh laundry on a chair and slipping it onto the pillow that Roy indicated.

'There you go, Mr Allen,' she said, passing the plumped up pillow to the old man.

'You're a good girl, hen, so you are.' He smacked his lips in appreciation and slid it behind his head.

'Come and have a seat,' Roy said, with a nod of his head. 'I can tell you're here for a reason.'

Doris grabbed her cloth bag and carefully took out the jug and the broken shards.

'I had a wee accident in the shop. I was hoping you could mend it?'

'Give it here, then.' Roy's gaze narrowed thoughtfully as he took his time looking at the jug.

Doris held her breath. It came out as a long whoosh when Roy finally nodded.

'Aye, I can fix that for you. A bit of glue and it'll be good as new.'

'Will it?' She brightened. Franny had to be pleased with that.

Roy laughed and ruffled her hair. 'I'm not a magician, Dor. You'll still see the cracks but it'll hold water.'

She loved it when he called her 'Dor'. Only Roy did that and it made her feel special and gave her a glow of happiness. She wasn't so sure about the hair ruffling. She'd seen him ruffle his little sister's hair too.

'You make yourself comfortable while I get the glue.'

He spread the pieces onto a sheet of newspaper and set to work. Doris was happy to watch him. It allowed her to soak in the sight of his tanned hands, so strong and yet so sensitive. He was able to fix just about anything. She loved watching the top of his head and the way the light from the window gave his dark hair a coppery glint. She looked up to see his grandad smiling at her. She looked away uncomfortably. She was certain he knew how she felt about Roy. She hoped he never came out and said it. His veiled jokes were bad enough.

'So, tell me what's happening in the world,' Roy said. 'Did you read the papers today?'

'Mr Churchill has announced amphibious operations on a grand scale. The headline is "*Zero Hour Approaching. Lampedusa points way to big events*",' Doris said eagerly.

'Now that is interesting.' Roy paused with the glue pot and brush. 'Lampedusa — that's an island, if I remember correctly. They'll be looking towards invading Sicily. That'll be the big event. I'll eat my hat if it's not.'

Doris stared in admiration at him. 'How did you know it's an island?'

'I may not be great at reading but I can look at an atlas and work out the names, if I've got time.'

'I didn't mean...'

'Course you didn't, Dor. I know that. The words all jumble up when I try to read the newspapers but if I get peace to sit with my atlas, it makes sense and I can work on the individual names. I get there in the end. Besides, we've got the wireless. Trouble is, with my work hours, I never get to hear the news properly. Only if Hugh puts it on down at the warehouse.'

'You might not read well but you've got a store of knowledge in your head. I wish I remembered half the stuff you do.'

'I like discussing the news with you,' Roy said. 'It's important to know what's going on. It shouldn't be just for the rich toffs and politicians. Ordinary folk like us need to take an interest. After the war, we'll be fighting for better wages, better living conditions and better jobs.'

'Yes, you're right.'

She felt his earnest enthusiasm infect her. If Roy was going to fight for all that, she'd do it too. Her thoughts flicked to her mother and her spirits dived. If Leila had her way, Doris wouldn't leave the house in case something happened.

'I wish I could've enlisted,' she said wistfully. 'Why do I have to have bad eyesight and asthma? It's not fair. I wanted to apply to the Wrens. And it wasn't just the lovely smart blue uniform, whatever people say. It's so I could make a real difference.'

'You're doing your bit. You work at Fearnmore, don't you? That's munitions works and essential to the war effort.'

'I'm a cleaner; I'm not on the factory floor making the shell casings. I applied and then when they saw how bad I can see, they gave me the cleaning job instead. It's hardly glamorous.'

'Glamorous isn't important but hard graft is,' Roy reminded her. He put down the mended jug and turned it gently. 'There we go. You'll need to leave it here to dry properly.'

'Thanks, Roy. I'm sorry to gripe about my own problems. I know you wanted to enlist too.'

Roy wiped his hands on the newspaper and looked at his print-blackened fingertips. Then he smiled at her.

'We're a right pair, you and me. I'd never heard of flat feet before my medical. And to top it off, I've got a heart murmur.'

'But they said it wasn't dangerous,' Doris said. 'That's true, isn't it?'

He laughed at the nervous tone in her voice. 'Aye, that's true. You're not getting rid of me that easily. But it's a bugger, excuse my language, because I can't get into the forces. I'd already imagined myself in khaki when that doctor shook his head. Now I'm working as a night watchman in the warehouses and picking up stinking bones and scrap metal for old man Stevenson in the days.'

'Both of those are vital to the war effort. After all, the warehouses are full of stuff we need. We owe it to the convoys and your dad to make sure it's safe.'

'You can say that, and it's true. Just as I can say to you that your work is valuable and it is. But when you want something so badly and you can't have it… that's beyond difficult to deal with some days.'

Yes, he was right about that, Doris thought, looking at his lovely, familiar face with a deep-down yearning. If she had the choice between being suddenly healthy enough to join the Wrens or pretty enough to capture Roy's male attention, she knew which one she'd choose.

'I feel no one wants me to leave home, either,' she said. 'Mum always goes on about being glad I'm there so I feel guilty for wanting to go. Franny said the same today. That she was glad I'd failed my medical so I could work in the shop.'

45

'I'd miss you too, if you went swanning off somewhere.'

'Would you?' Doris whispered.

Their gazes met and for a brief second something flared in his eyes. A loud snore reverberated round the room and Roy burst out laughing. Jock Allen was slumped asleep in his rocking chair. The snores grew louder.

'Like a foghorn, so he is,' Roy chuckled. 'See why I can't sleep afternoons?'

Doris picked up the tartan blanket which had slipped off the old man's knees and tucked it back around him.

'I'd best be off. I like to help Mum prepare the tea before I go to the factory. Thanks for mending the jug.'

'That's what pals are for. And you're my best pal, Dor.' He ruffled her hair again.

'You're mine too, Roy.'

It was hopeless. For Roy, she was the girl next door and his best friend. Would she ever have the courage to say out loud the words that pulsed through every heartbeat?

*I am deeply and irreversibly in love with you, Roy Allen*, she said silently as she waved and smiled and went down the steps and across to her own flat.

# Chapter Four

The war was dragging on and, with the likelihood of an Allied invasion of France increasing as the months ticked by, hundreds of landing craft were being built on Clydeside. The shipyards were flourishing, and those that had closed during the Great Depression were open for business once again, making Glasgow a bustling place to live and work, especially down by the docklands.

But in Kiltie Street, Elsie was more concerned with the heat of the summer weather.

The Weirs' flat was hot and stuffy but Louise refused to open the windows.

'I'm freezing. See the goose pimples on my arms. Aren't you cold, too?'

'It's a lovely sunny day,' Elsie said with a concerned frown. 'It's boiling in here, Ma. I'm worried that you can't feel that.'

Jessie's face was flushed shiny pink as she sat on the floor playing with her paper dolls.

'I'm too hot,' she whined. 'Can we open the door and fan it?'

'I've told you, we're not opening anything. I'm fair shivering here,' Louise snapped.

'Take your dolls and play outside,' Elsie suggested to her little sister.

Jessie shook her head sullenly. 'It's too hot out there as well. There's no shade and I've nobody to play with. Isa's away on a farm and she's my best friend.'

'What about the other girls at school? I bet you've made some nice friends by now.'

'I haven't. I told you and you're not listening to me. Everyone's got a best friend and a group to hang about with already. Mrs Black told me to stop putting my hand up in class to answer questions and let someone else have a turn.'

'Why did she do that?'

Jessie shrugged. 'It's boring. I've done it all in the village school and Auntie Alison taught me stuff too. Everyone was mean about me answering all the time. They said I was a teacher's pet. And I'm not.'

'Of course you're not. It's good you know your lessons,' Elsie said.

'I want to go back to Auntie Alison and Uncle Donald and my room. Mrs Potter brings me cold drinks when it's hot and my books are there.'

'Shhh, don't let Ma hear you say that, she'll be so upset.'

Elsie glanced over but Louise had fallen asleep again in the armchair. Jessie sniffled, wiping snot from her nose with the back of her hand.

'Here, mop your nose with this.'

Elsie gave her a handkerchief from her pocket, feeling tired and worn out. Jessie had been home for a month and it hadn't been easy. The flat felt too small for the three of them now that Jessie was so tall. They had a room and kitchen which normally would be home to a whole family but Elsie was only too conscious of how different it was from the Cranstons' large house and how Jessie must be feeling.

Not that Jessie complained much. She didn't need to. Her expression of revulsion at the soot-blackened windows, the threadbare armchair and the washing hung on the pulley was plain. She spoke less cheerfully, seeming to draw in on herself. Her skin had lost its glow and Elsie was sure she'd lost some weight. The rations were so tight these days and they didn't have the benefit of living in the countryside where there was extra food to be had.

While she fretted about Jessie, there was also Louise to worry about. She refused to see the doctor, claiming they couldn't afford it. That was true but Elsie knew it was more than that. Ma was frightened. She didn't want to hear what the doctor would tell her.

Louise mumbled in her sleep then woke up with a cry and bent over vomiting. Elsie ran to her.

'Get the bucket,' she shouted to Jessie. 'Ma, are you all right? Talk to me.'

She put her hand on her mother's forehead. She was burning up. She stared at Elsie as if she didn't know her. Jessie ran through with their iron bucket and a cloth and Elsie held Ma's hair back as she was sick again. She washed the floor, glad they had linoleum and not carpet and tried not to feel sick herself at the smell.

'Why's she sick?' Jessie said, wrapping her arms round her body and rocking.

'It's the drink, she can't handle it any more. Go outside and get some fresh air. I'll just clean this up and make Ma comfortable. Go on now.'

Jessie ran out.

'My head… my head's spinning…' Ma moaned.

'It's all right, I'm here. Rest back in the chair. That's it. I'll call for Doctor Graham.'

With surprising strength, Ma gripped her wrist. 'No, I won't have him here.'

'You're sick. That's the third funny turn you've had this week. I don't like the look of you.'

'I've got something to tell you…'

'Well, whatever it is can wait. Let me get you a glass of water.'

'Listen to me. Just let me catch my breath,' Ma wheezed.

Her fingers still clutched at Elsie's wrist, holding on so tight that she felt Ma's nails digging into her skin. She waited, hearing the ragged breathing and wishing she could at least move the bucket and its vile contents. She thought Ma had fallen asleep again but when she moved, Ma lifted her face to gaze straight into her eyes.

'I'm not going to be here much longer,' she said.

When Elsie shook her head, Ma lifted her palm.

'We're not going to argue about this. I know… I know what I'm saying… what I can feel inside.'

'Please don't do this,' Elsie said, a lump forming in her throat. 'We can talk later.'

'We have to talk now. I have to tell you.'

'Tell me what? There's nothing I need to hear. I love you, Ma,' she sobbed.

'I love you too, darling girl and I love my wee Jessie.'

'You're going to get better. I don't care what you say, I'm getting Doctor Graham and he'll give you medicine and you'll be fine. As right as rain.'

'Love, you have to listen. I'm tired and there's not much time. Will you do that for me?'

There was a weariness in Ma's voice that brought Elsie up short. She nodded.

'When I'm gone, I don't want you two being alone. I know I told you my parents were dead and I've no brothers and sisters but it wasn't true. You've got a grandmother and aunts and an uncle all living in Kiltie Street.'

Elsie sprang to her feet and looked at Ma in shock. Was this another of her lies? She looked serious but it was hard to tell.

'It's true,' Louise said. 'This time it's true.'

'How can they live in Kiltie Street and you've never told us? How could you!'

'There was a falling-out a long time ago. You were only toddling. I'm not going to explain it but try to understand I did what was best for you.'

'Does everyone else in Kiltie Street know? They must do. It must be the best kept secret in the street,' Elsie said bitterly.

'It was no one's business but our own. Folk can keep their mouths shut if they need to,' Louise said. 'They wouldn't want to hurt you or Jessie by letting it slip.'

'Who is she? Which of our neighbours is my grandmother?' Elsie could hardly believe it.

'You've never met her properly. She's called Isobel Mearns. She lives at the top of number one.'

Isobel Mearns. Elsie rolled the name around in her mind. It didn't bring back any memories. If she'd been a toddler when the argument happened, wouldn't she have memories of her granny cuddling her or singing to her?

'My mother wasn't the kind to cuddle,' Louise said, when Elsie put that to her. 'I don't think she ever picked you up or sang to you. Spare the rod and spoil the child was the way she brought us up.'

'I'm going for a walk,' Elsie said. 'I need time to think about all this. It's too much to take in.'

'I'll have a wee nap and when you're back, we can talk some more,' Louise said, closing her eyes.

Elsie studied the delicate blue veins like lace on Ma's eyelids. There was a fragility to her in recent days, as if she would break apart if shaken. She bit her lip on another sob. A walk was the answer. She went out into the bright, warm evening. Jessie was sitting on the pavement making her paper dolls chat to each other.

'Have you come to play with me?' she asked.

'In a while. I just need to walk up the street a bit. I'll be back soon. Don't go back in, Ma's resting.'

Elsie walked fast along Kiltie Street, past the worn out muddy grass opposite the tenements, now baked hard in the summer sun, past the bench at the entrance to the street with its buckled wooden slats which had seen better days. Up the steep hill she went, climbing towards the large sandstone houses with the trees, their leaves rippling in the breeze. Usually she liked being here. Her glance took in the house at the end where she'd bought the gin and she turned on her heel.

In the end, she walked along the river bank where it was peaceful. An old man went by with two dogs tethered together with rope, and a woman cycled past wearing a straw hat with a turquoise ribbon. Elsie was angry. Angry with Ma. How could she have lied over something so huge? She was used to her little lies, smoothing things over so there was no confrontation. Lies for an easy life. But this... a whole family that Elsie didn't know about! Not only that but a family that lived in the same tenement row. She must've passed her aunts and uncle and granny hundreds of times over the years. Did they know who she was? Of course they must.

She grabbed at the long grasses beside the water, tearing them out by the roots and breaking them in her hands without thought. Eventually, she sank down into the grass and cried. She lay there, out of sight, staring at the blue sky above. Then she sat up. That was enough. She had Jessie to think of. She had to be told too at some point. Elsie couldn't bear to do that now. It was all too raw.

'Come in and help me make the tea now, you can peel the tatties,' she said to Jessie as she got back to Kiltie Street.

Reluctantly, Jessie gathered up her dolls and their outfits and followed her inside.

Ma was motionless, slumped in the armchair. Elsie's insides lurched. She rushed over and shook her shoulder. Louise mumbled in her sleep and, with relief, Elsie tiptoed into the kitchen. For a moment, she'd thought her mother had passed. She took down the packet of dried eggs from the shelf and began to organise their meal. Any more questions would have to wait.

For a couple of weeks, Louise Weir rallied. She stopped drinking and started taking care of herself. She dressed neatly and went out of the flat to the shops. Elsie was surprised to come home, tired from her shift at the munitions factory, to discover a small plate of pork chops or a cabbage that Ma proudly presented for their tea. Jessie was happier, too. She cuddled in to Ma, asking for stories before bed and chattered away to her, telling her about school and about the village in Perthshire.

On the Thursday near the end of June when Elsie had a rare day off, Louise insisted on going out for sausages.

'I was going to make a Woolton pie today,' Elsie said. 'Why don't you rest instead?'

'Because I fancy sausages for my tea. It won't take me long. Besides, the butcher and me, we've got an agreement. He keeps a few nice cuts under the counter for special customers. I won't be long.'

Elsie rolled her eyes. Trust Ma to have wangled special treatment. She didn't think buying on the black market was wrong even after Elsie had argued with her about it. She busied herself putting the kettle on the range to heat. They could have a nice cup of tea when Ma got back. She hummed the tune of 'Little Brown Jug' as she worked. It was nice to have a break from the factory floor with its noise and clamour.

She heard the door open and close and called out a greeting. Ma came through and sat at the kitchen table.

'I'll have a cuppa if it's on the go,' Louise said. 'I'm that tired.'

Elsie poured the boiling water onto the few leaves in the old teapot. She turned to put it on the table and it slipped from her hands.

'Ma?'

Louise's chin was on her chest and her body had slid to the side of the chair. She was gone. Elsie knew that instantly; she hardly needed to check. There was a stillness, an absence of spirit. She put her fingers to Ma's mouth anyway, hoping to feel her breath. Nothing. She ran out of the flat and down the stone stairs and out into the street looking for help. Glancing frantically both ways, she saw a tall figure in dark blue passing at the end of the street.

Elsie ran towards him. 'Help, I need help.'

The policeman stopped. She had an impression of blond hair and green eyes under his special constable's peaked cap.

'What is it, Miss? What's the matter?' An English voice, like in the Pathé News she saw at the cinema.

'Please come, it's Ma... it's my mother. She's dead.'

He didn't ask her more but followed quickly as Elsie led the way into number eight and up the communal stairway, turning right into their flat. He knelt down and felt for a pulse in Louise's neck and wrist. Then he looked up at Elsie and shook his head.

Elsie was too numb to cry. 'Jessie... my sister... she'll be home soon from school. I don't want her to see Ma like this.'

'I'm going to call for the doctor. I won't be long. Will you be all right until I come back?' he asked.

She nodded. All she remembered later that night was a blur of images. Doctor Graham was there and the young constable and finally the undertaker. Jessie, clutching her teddy and sucking her thumb as if she was five. Mrs Woodley, Jeannie's mother, bringing them a pot of stew and asking if they wanted to stay the night at number four. She'd shaken her head at that. She didn't want to leave Ma on her own.

The coffin lay across three of the kitchen chairs in the parlour. It didn't seem right to have it lie on the floor. Mrs Woodley and another woman from the street had washed and laid her out. Elsie, sitting in vigil, thought how pretty Ma was, her face relaxed and the worry lines erased in death. She held her hand and talked to her, telling her all the things she wished she'd said before.

'Go and get your nightie on,' she said to Jessie. 'Don't forget to brush your teeth.'

'Are we sleeping in the kitchen tonight?'

'We'll sleep in our own bed in the parlour as usual.'

'But... Ma is in there,' Jessie said, biting her nails.

'There's nothing to be afraid of,' Elsie said gently, putting an arm around her. 'It's only Ma. I want to keep her company.'

Jessie nodded. She brushed her teeth at the Belfast sink and washed her face. She climbed into their recess bed and Elsie got in too. It was early for her to sleep but she knew Jessie needed her. They held each other until Jessie fell asleep and Elsie was left with her frantic thoughts. How would they cope now that Ma was gone? She'd said that Isobel Mearns would take them in but, despite neighbours popping in during the evening, no one had come and said they were family. She was hit suddenly by a rush of grief, her tears dripping down onto the pillow, making it damp. Ma was gone. She was never going to grab Elsie and swing her round the room while crooning the 'Skye Boat Song'. She was never going to surprise her by dressing up that occasional way she had in her best dress and hat to 'take the air', as she had put it. She even missed Ma's low moods when she curled in the chair and wouldn't be roused to smile. At least even then she had been in their wee home with Elsie. For two years it had been just the two of them, keeping each other company in the evenings.

What was going to happen now? She was gripped by a different kind of fear. How was she going to pay the rent on their flat? Ma had contributed what she called her widow's pension although they were never told what their father's job had been. Her wage, though generous at the munitions factory, wasn't enough and she wouldn't make Jessie go into service. There was something very young about her sister despite her being thirteen. Elsie knew she would only worry horribly if Jessie ended up as a live-in scullery maid.

The Mearns didn't arrive in the next three days, either. Different people came and sat with Louise as was the tradition. Elsie still had to go to work and she insisted that Jessie go to school on Friday. Meals were provided by the women who lived nearby and Mrs Woodley came and cleaned the house. Elsie didn't know how to thank them all.

'There's no need for that,' Mary Woodley said. 'We look after our own in Kiltie Street. One day, you'll be doing that for me or for Mrs Lennox or whoever. That's how you show your thanks.'

She opened the window and covered the hall mirror with a shawl.

'So her soul finds its way,' she said, though Elsie hadn't asked.

The curtains were shut out of respect and all the neighbouring flats did likewise.

Ma had been paying for her own funeral over the years, a little every month, Elsie discovered. She'd paid enough that it covered the cost of a black hearse with its glass cover and coal-black horses with tall plumes. The minister came up and said prayers and local men carried the coffin down to the waiting hearse.

Their home was full of women and children. The women prepared a meal for when the men came back from the cemetery. Elsie, dressed in black, found she had little to do. Jessie, also in black, played with the children quietly, looking glad to be included for once.

'I can make ham sandwiches,' Elsie offered, squeezing past a small group of women fussing with a meat pie and a plate of scones with margarine.

So much kindness, it almost overwhelmed her. They were all living on rations that left them hungry these days

57

and yet they had all contributed to the wake. She didn't even know them all well.

'Aye, you can do that,' one woman said kindly. 'Here's a knife and a clean plate. Mrs O'Leary brought the bit of ham. It'll stretch if you cut it thinly, like.'

She was concentrating on slicing the ham wafer thin and trying to work out how many sandwiches she could make when Mrs Woodley called her.

'Someone's asking for you, dear. She won't come in. She's in the hall.' Mrs Woodley looked as if she would say more but then shook her head quickly, patted Elsie on the shoulder and gave her a gentle push towards the hall.

The women glanced curiously at her as she went past them but busied themselves with their tasks. She heard Mrs Woodley saying something in a low tone but couldn't hear what she said. Out in the hall stood a tall, thin woman with a pinched face.

'Elspeth Weir?' she said.

'That's right. How can I help you?'

Elsie smoothed her black dress down and hoped her hair was neat. She wasn't used to hearing her full name as friends and family all called her Elsie. There was a sharpness to the other woman's gaze that made her nervous. She recognised her from walking past her in the street but they had never spoken.

'So, you're Louise's girl. You're the spit of her, now I see you up close, I'll say that for you.' The voice was sneering and Elsie took a step back.

'Who are you?' But she knew the answer. She had to be one of the Mearns family, Ma's relatives. The well-kept secret that pervaded Kiltie Street, out of kindness and respect for Louise, Elsie and Jessie.

'I'm your Aunt Ada. You've to come with me and meet your grandmother.'

'I can't leave now. There's the wake.' And she didn't want to, all of a sudden.

'And bring the other girl with you.'

Ada Mearns was already on her way out as if she hadn't heard Elsie.

'Who was that?' Jessie asked, coming up with another girl who had her paper dolls in a grubby hand.

'We need to go,' Elsie said. 'Just for a wee while and then we'll be back for the wake when the men arrive.'

She took Jessie's hand and they walked across to the first tenement in the row. Ada Mearns was waiting for them at the foot of the stairs.

'We live on the top floor. We've got five rooms.' Ada puffed her chest out.

'Five rooms; they must be rich,' Jessie whispered to Elsie as they followed their aunt's ramrod back up the immaculate stairs.

At the top floor door, they hesitated until Ada waved them impatiently inside. The hall smelt of lemons and beeswax and unstirred air.

'Go into the parlour,' Ada ordered them.

Inside, in a room crammed with ornaments and soft cushions, a large walnut-cased wireless and a wide fireplace, two women were sitting. The older one was dressed in black, her white hair drawn back in a severe bun, a walking stick leaning against the chair. The younger one had pale yellow hair and faded blue eyes and the hint of a smile when she saw them.

'Louise's children, I must suppose,' Isobel Mearns said.

Elsie was searching for memories or at least for some sort of recognition from passing this old lady in the street. But there was nothing.

'I'm Elspeth and this is Jessie,' she said with more confidence than she felt.

She wasn't going to let the old dragon have it all her own way. If she had smiled at them or made some show of feeling then she might have felt more warmly towards her.

'What age are you?' Isobel said abruptly.

'What business is it of yours?' Elsie cried.

'You're a cheeky young madam. It's all my business if you're living under my roof. Now answer the question.'

Biting down on a rude reply, Elsie told her. She knew she couldn't afford to get on her wrong side. There was no way she could pay for the rent on their home. She'd done the sums several times and it just wasn't possible. It looked as if living with their grandmother was the only solution. She knew she ought to be thankful that they were being offered a place to stay. It was an answer to her desperate prayers and surely a kindness being offered by her newly found relatives.

'Twenty-four and not yet married. You want to be careful you don't get left on the shelf. If you were married, you wouldn't be in the pickle that you're in.'

'We're sorry for your loss,' the younger woman said in the silence that followed that remark. 'I'm your Aunt Sarah.'

'Thank you,' Elsie murmured.

She felt sure she'd seen her aunt before, perhaps at the shops or walking along Kiltie Street. How odd it was to think their paths had crossed and she didn't know they were tied by blood.

'Come back tomorrow when the funeral is over and we'll discuss the living arrangements,' Isobel said, with a black look at Sarah until the younger woman seemed to wilt.

Ada appeared as if she'd been listening at the door, and showed them out. In a few minutes they were back at their own home. There was noisy chatter wafting out of the flat. Before they went in, Elsie gripped Jessie's hand.

'It's going to be all right. I promise you.'

'I don't like them. Who are they?'

'Our grandmother and our aunts. I'll explain it all to you later. Right now, we have to put on a good face for our guests and make sure everyone has enough to eat and drink. We're going to celebrate Ma's life and give her a good send-off.'

It was even busier in the flat now that the men were back. After an hour or so, families left, shaking Elsie's hands and telling her that if she needed them, she only had to ask. Soon, only Mrs Woodley and Mrs O'Leary were there, tidying up and wrapping the small amount of leftover food to put on the cold slab.

'Thank you so much,' Elsie said gratefully as the two women went out the door.

She sank into Ma's armchair, glad of the peace and quiet. Jessie had asked to go and play with the other children and she'd agreed. She hoped their friendliness would continue but had a sneaky feeling they had been put on their best behaviour by their mothers and told to be nice to the girl whose mother had died.

There was a knock on the door. Elsie wanted to scream. Was she to get no time to herself at all? Opening it, she saw a tall policeman and gasped. What was wrong?

'Sorry, I didn't mean to startle you. I came to offer my condolences. Special Constable Cooper, or you can call me Fred.'

He took off his dark blue cap with its shiny chrome badge and Elsie recognised him then as the policeman who had helped her the day Ma had died.

'You can come in,' she said, noting again his dark blond hair and green eyes. 'I never got a chance to thank you properly for helping me when Ma... collapsed. I don't know what I'd have done if you hadn't been passing. Are you new here?' she asked. 'Where's Tam Macrae, who used to be on this beat?'

'Tam enlisted and is away in the army. I'm a special constable covering some of Tam's ground.'

'You're not local?'

'Hard to hide that with my London accent.' His grin faded away and he looked concerned. 'Seriously, how are you coping? You were distraught that day when you found your mother gone.'

'I can't believe she has gone. There's a lot to sort out but I'll manage.'

She wasn't going to tell him about her newly discovered family. That was all too strange to share with anyone. He looked as if was going to say something more but jammed his cap onto his head.

'Best be off before the sergeant comes looking. He has to sign my notebook twice in my shift and I doubt popping in here counts as work.'

He grinned again and she thought how young he was. Not much older than herself. It was kind of him to look in on her. She showed him out and then scrubbed the kitchen floor even though it didn't need it as the women had cleaned it that morning.

Two men with a horse and cart stopped by the next morning. Elsie saw them from the window and wondered who they were visiting. There was a clattering on the stairs and a loud knock on her door.

'Landlord sent us.' The men brushed past her.

'What are you doing?'

'Taking the furniture. He needs it elsewhere.'

'But you can't. It's ours!'

'Sorry, hen. We're just following orders.'

'There's been a mistake,' Elsie said desperately. 'Don't take that. It's my mother's sideboard. She was proud of it.'

'It was all rented, hen. Didn't you know that? Now let us do our work. We've another job after this an' all.'

Elsie was glad that Jessie wasn't there to see the destruction of their home. It took the two men less than a half hour to move all the furniture out. They even took the decrepit armchair. She watched them move it as the stuffing drifted out onto the stairwell.

Later, she went to meet Jessie from St Mildred's school. She saw her sister dragging her feet across the playground as the other children ran out in groups, shouting and laughing at the end of the school day. Jessie brightened when she saw her.

'Why are you here?' Jessie smiled. 'You never come and meet me from school.'

'We're going to live with our grandmother so I thought I'd fetch you. We can go straight there.'

'What about our clothes and my books?'

'I've got them packed. We've got 'til tomorrow to collect them from the flat.'

Jessie walked happily alongside her although Elsie was dreading it. She smiled at her sister. They both hesitated at the bottom of the steps to number one, Kiltie Street.

'This is our new life,' Elsie said. 'Up we go.'

Aunt Ada opened the door with a dour stare. 'She's expecting you. Go on through.'

Determined not to be browbeaten, Elsie fixed a smile to her face and took Jessie's hand as they went into the large, cluttered parlour. Isobel Mearns was sitting where they'd last seen her and Elsie wondered if she had moved at all. Then Isobel got up, leaning stiffly on her stick. She motioned for them to follow her and pointed at a doorway next to the parlour.

'You will have that room there. My son, Leo, has just moved out to live with his new wife. That was his room. No one can say that Isobel Mearns hasn't done her duty in taking in her orphan granddaughters.'

Elsie pushed open the door and gasped in dismay. It was completely empty apart from a pair of drab brown curtains hanging from a rail at the window. The bare floorboards had wisps of carpet caught on nails where it had been recently removed.

'We don't have any furniture; it was all rented,' she said, turning to her grandmother.

'That isn't my problem. You should think yourselves lucky to have a roof over your heads.'

She turned away into the parlour, leaving them standing there. When Elsie glanced round, she saw Ada's smirk before the woman vanished into the kitchen.

'Come on, Jessie. Let's go and see the view from the window. We'll make it our own, I promise. Once we get our belongings, it'll look much better.'

She wasn't going to let Jessie see her tears. She had an awful sense that things were going to get worse before they got any better.

# Chapter Five

Elsie's head was thick with tiredness. She sat in the munitions factory canteen at dinnertime, eating fish-paste sandwiches on dry bread that curled at the edges. Beside her, Jeannie leaned across the table, explaining to Ruby how she'd added embroidery to her skirt to make it feel like a new outfit. Letty and Barbara were giggling together but Elsie felt quite alone. Jeannie always asked her to join them at the meal break in the factory but she wasn't quite one of the gang.

The problem went way back to when she was fifteen and Jeannie's brother Jimmy was sixteen. She had had an embarrassing crush on him and followed him about everywhere. He took a real dislike to her and she didn't blame him. She had been a pest. She knew it was awkward for Jeannie to be too friendly with her now.

To be honest, if she'd had other friends on the factory floor, she'd have sat with them instead. But she hadn't really found anyone that she connected with. It didn't matter now. Jessie was her main concern.

They had had an uncomfortable night. Elsie had gathered all their clothes for a makeshift mattress and, swallowing her pride, begged Aunt Ada for a blanket to cover them. She tossed and turned all night, unable to sleep. Beside her, Jessie moaned in her sleep and curled in towards her.

In the morning, Elsie woke Jessie early and helped her find clothes for school that were not too creased from being lain on. She went through to the kitchen where Aunt Ada was stirring porridge in a pan on the range.

'Good morning,' she said politely, determined to start their new life well and knowing she had to get on Ada's good side, if there was such a thing.

'You'll be wanting porridge, no doubt,' Ada said sourly, ignoring her greeting.

She dumped two bowls on the scrubbed table without another word. Elsie nodded to Jessie to eat. She had a sudden fear that if they didn't scrape their porridge quickly into their mouths, Aunt Ada would take it away. The two girls ate in silence, the atmosphere tense.

'Good morning, did you sleep well?' Aunt Sarah appeared, smiling.

'Yes, thank you,' Elsie said politely.

Their younger aunt didn't appear to realise they had no bed to sleep in. She sat at the table with them and Ada put down another bowl of steaming hot porridge and a jug of milk. Sarah poured some into her own bowl and offered it to Jessie.

'Don't you want milk?'

Jessie nodded shyly and Sarah poured it. Elsie wanted to say that they hadn't been offered any by Aunt Ada but instead she accepted a generous pool of it in her bowl, making the porridge float and quiver.

'Don't spoil them, Sarah,' Aunt Ada snapped. 'They are here on charity and must get used to it.'

Sarah's smile vanished and she ate her own portion quietly.

'Have you seen to Mother this morning?' Ada asked.

'She's still asleep. I'll go as soon as I've eaten this,' Sarah said.

Elsie thought she looked almost afraid of Ada. Sarah stood up, her porridge not yet finished.

'Eat that up,' Ada said. 'It's a sin to waste good food.'

Obediently, Sarah sat again and scraped her bowl clean before hurrying out with a quick, sympathetic glance at Elsie.

'Thank you,' Elsie said, taking their bowls to the Belfast sink to wash.

'Leave those. That's my job. You may as well learn the house rules right now.' Aunt Ada put down the ladle beside the spotless range and stared at them both. 'My responsibilities are the housework, the shopping and cooking. Sarah is Mother's companion. My mother never leaves the house; she can't manage the stairs. You will do what you are told. I will have tasks for you and Sarah may ask you to help her. You may go now.'

Elsie felt Aunt Ada's dark eyes boring into her back as they left the kitchen. She deliberately walked slowly although she wanted to run. Aunt Ada wanted to intimidate them, that was obvious. Elsie wasn't going to show that it was working.

'I don't want to come back here after school,' Jessie whispered.

'You have to. I'm sorry but this is our home now. Ma would want us to stay together. I wish it was all different. Now, I've got to rush or I'll miss the bus. We've got each other and that's all that matters.'

Her words echoed in her head now as the other women in the canteen laughed and talked. They had each other but was it enough?

'A penny for them?' Jeannie said.

'Hmm?'

Jeannie laughed. 'That's what I mean. You're miles away. Everything all right?'

'Of course it is. Why shouldn't it be?' Elsie said abruptly.

There was no way she could explain her awful home situation to anyone, let alone these girls who were all full of laughter and jokes and who didn't really know her.

'Keep your hat on. I was only asking,' Jeannie said stiffly.

'Oh, I didn't...'

But Jeannie had turned away from her and started a conversation with Barbara. Elsie miserably took her dirty plate and mug back to the canteen workers. Perhaps she'd blown it even with Jeannie's little group. There was a part of her that didn't care. She had too many other problems. The main one was how she was to get some furniture for their room.

—

Annie had also had a sleepless night. She felt as if someone was taking a hammer to her temples. Davey had cried for three hours solidly in the night. She tried soothing him but he simply yelled louder. She tried feeding him but he squirmed away from her breast. Paul had yelled at her too and stomped from their bed into the kitchen, slamming the door loudly. She looked resentfully at the baby, sleeping peacefully now in his drawer.

'Every bloody evening and every bloody night. What is the matter with you?' she said, and then felt guilty for swearing at him.

In fact, feeling guilty was becoming a daily emotion that rippled through her, making her sweat smell acrid in the warm, muggy weather. Remembering how she'd wished she had never had Davey made her shiver with guilt. How could she have said that about her own child? She wasn't fit to be a mother. And, if she knew that, she bet that everyone else knew it, too. Ivy let her know it every day.

'Give him to me. You're useless at holding his head. If you don't hold him properly, he'll grow up with a floppy neck,' Ivy said later that day.

'I'm holding him properly.'

Her mother tutted, taking Davey from her arms and crooning at him. 'That's better. Watch how I do it. You know, when Brian was a wee baby, I used to hold him for hours like this.'

'It's a wonder you got any housework done then,' Annie said.

'It's all about being organised.' Ivy cast her eye critically round the small kitchen. 'Looks as if you could learn a bit about that.'

'Don't you have things to do at your house? You don't have to come up here every day.'

'As long as I'm home in the evenings, Brian can find me if he turns up. Mornings I've got my WVS work at the centre and afternoons I can always find time for my grandson. Besides, you need the help, whether you know it or not. He's grizzling. Time for a feed.'

'I'm not a cow but I feel like one, getting milked every hour.'

'Don't be daft. Give him a feed.' Ivy's black brows beetled and Annie sighed.

She sat and fed Davey while Ivy made a deal out of cleaning the kitchen.

'Where's that useless husband of yours?'

'Paul's gone out looking for work,' Annie lied.

She had no idea where he was. He didn't bother to tell her whenever he went out. All she knew was that so far there was no sign of employment. He didn't return until Ivy had left later that afternoon.

'I've prepared the tatties and left them in the pot covered in cold water and there's a wee bit of meat on the cold slab, I've wrapped it in a damp cloth. Give me my boy for a kiss and I'll be away.'

Ivy's handbag and coat were in the hall ready. It might be high summer and a hot day but she wouldn't be seen dead without those and her hat and gloves. Annie watched her kiss Davey's soft head.

'Thanks, Mum.'

The eyebrows shot up. 'I'm your mother, Annie Morris, and that's why I'm here to help.'

'Annie Thom, now. Remember I'm married to Paul.' She had been about to be grateful to her mother but now she just felt annoyed.

'Right then. I'll be up again tomorrow.' Ivy put on her coat and picked up her bulging handbag and went out. She paused in the doorway. 'You should get out with Davey. He needs fresh air. It's not good for him, being cooped up in here all the time.'

'I don't have a pram.'

'Plenty of girls don't have prams. They're so scarce these days in the shops – let alone the price of them. It'd be a miracle if you did! You'll have to use the old methods. I used to put you in my shawl and wrap it round me.'

With that last instruction, Ivy disappeared and Annie heard her heavy footsteps on the stairway. She stared at Davey. They had hardly been out of the flat since he was born. She didn't need to. Ivy brought the shopping and

Paul, for all his faults, could be relied on to go out if they desperately needed something. Maybe her mum was right. If it stopped Davey's terrible crying in the evenings and nights, it was worth a try.

She got up and found her old tartan shawl. Usually she wore it over her nightgown when the evenings got too cold. She wrapped it round her dress and nestled Davey into it before tying it securely at the back. He gurgled and Annie smiled and tickled his chin. She had her hands free. Her mum had a point. The old ways worked. She walked carefully down the stairs and out into the sunny day. A short walk might benefit them both.

Paul walked towards her, grinning. A jolt of desire shot through her.

'I've bought you something,' he said.

Her heart sank and the desire fled. They had little money. What they did have had to be spent on food and rent.

'What did you buy?'

'I've bought us a new bed. Look, here's the cart now.'

'Oh, Paul, why did you do that? There's nothing wrong with the old bed and we can't afford it. Tell him to take it back.'

His grin vanished, to be replaced by a dark scowl. 'I'll do nothing of the sort. It's bought and paid for.'

'With what? Where did you get the money from? We've barely enough to pay the rent man this month,' she cried.

'You've turned into your mother. A right nag. I'm the man of the house and don't you forget it. Move aside and let me and the helper get it up the stairs,' Paul growled.

Speechless, she moved as a cart and horse swerved in to the kerb and the two men unlashed the new bed and hefted it up the steps. She could barely see through tears of humiliation. Several women, out sweeping their doorsteps, stared at her. She didn't know them, being so new to Kiltie Street, but it felt as if they were all judging her.

She walked away, glancing back to see their old bed being brought down and lashed to the cart. She saw Paul giving the cart man something and shook her head bitterly. It had to be their cash. She tried hard to save a little each week and here he was, throwing it away on a bed they didn't need. She dreaded to think what Ivy would say when she heard about it.

She heard the cart man saying loudly he'd be back in a while to take the bed away. He put a nosebag on the horse and sauntered away, whistling. She guessed he was going to the pub. It was embarrassing; their marital bed, sitting in the street like that for everyone to stare at.

The bed was still there after teatime. She and Paul had shared a silent meal. She was so angry she couldn't bring herself to speak to him. He didn't appear to care. He shovelled down his food and went out. Annie fed and washed Davey and put him down to sleep in his drawer. She couldn't help it. She walked down onto the pavement to look at the bed.

A young woman was walking along Kiltie Street. She slowed as she arrived at the cart with the bed gloriously high for the world and its wife to see. Annie glanced at her. She knew who she was but had never spoken to her.

'Is that yours?' Elsie asked.

'It was but not any more. You work at Fearnmore don't you? You get the bus with Jeannie Dougal.'

'That's right. I've seen you at Fearnmore too but we've never been on the same part of the floor.'

'Annie Thom. Pleased to meet you properly.'

'Elspeth Weir but my friends call me Elsie. I'm living at number one now, else I wouldn't be going past your bed. I didn't know you lived in Kiltie Street. You didn't used to, did you?'

Annie shook her head. 'We only moved in last month. Jeannie said there was a flat going for rent and my husband and I were looking to move out of my mum's place and get our own place now we've got the baby.'

'The thing is… although me and my sister have moved in with our grandmother's family, we don't have a bed.'

'You want this one?'

'How much would you want for it?' Elsie asked.

'Five shillings.'

Annie had no idea how much a bed cost but it looked as if Elsie was eager to buy. She knew she ought to ask Paul if she could sell it on but she was still furious with him.

'Oh, that's disappointing. I can't afford that much. My mum died recently and there's only my wage coming in.'

'I'm sorry, I didn't know that. Look, take the bed. We don't need it but you do.'

'You're so kind. I don't know how I can ever repay you,' Elsie said.

'How are you going to get it up to your flat?' Annie frowned. 'It's quite heavy.'

'I'm going to ask Special Constable Cooper to help.' Elsie pointed behind Annie with a wide smile.

Annie turned round to see a tall policeman headed their way. He grinned at Elsie and touched his cap to Annie.

'Good evening, ladies. What's all this? It can't stay here. The cart is blocking the road.'

As Kiltie Street was a dead end and motor cars rarely graced its surface, Annie thought that was a bit rich but Elsie seemed happy to see the policeman and he certainly was the solution to their problem of moving the bed.

'Good evening, Constable Cooper,' Elsie said. 'If you can help, we need to move the bed from the cart to the top floor of number one.'

Fred Cooper removed his cap and scratched his head for a moment. 'I need another man to help lift it.'

'Nonsense,' Annie said briskly. 'Elsie and I are quite capable of lifting a side, if you can take the other.'

She felt an unusual surge of energy. Here was a diversion, nothing to do with babies or breast milk or angry husbands. An activity that simply required two fit young women to aid a handsome policeman. She might be married but Annie's eyesight hadn't suffered. Special Constable Cooper was gorgeous. Not as handsome as Paul, of course, but much nicer in personality, she thought grimly.

'Let's give it a go,' Fred said.

He untied the ropes and between them, they managed to get the bed off the cart and onto the pavement. He was considering the best way to lift it when Martin O'Leary from number four came over.

'Do you need a hand, son?' Martin asked.

He was a grizzled older man and Fred hesitated.

'I'm strong as an ox,' Martin said. 'I was a welder in the shipyards when I was younger.'

Fred nodded and the four of them carried the bed along the street and up the stairs. It wasn't easy, as the stairs curved and the bed had a rigid iron frame, but they got there. A stern woman met them at the door.

'I've got a bed for my room, Aunt Ada,' Elsie said to her.

Ada stood aside and they handled the bed into an empty room. Annie was shocked to see there was no carpet or linoleum on the floorboards, nor any other furniture. She was glad she'd given the bed to Elsie for nothing. The poor girl obviously had no money. Someone was worse off than Annie herself. She felt the familiar guilt with that passing thought. She shouldn't be glad of Elsie's poverty.

What Annie found strange was that the rest of the flat spoke of some wealth. The hall was carpeted and a glance into the open parlour showed ornaments and a three-piece suite in flowered upholstery. She caught a glimpse of an old lady inside but the door was quickly closed by a fair-haired woman.

'Thank you all so much,' Elsie said. 'I'd love to offer you a drink but it's not my house and I haven't bought any food or drink yet.'

How odd, Annie thought. Still, it wasn't her business. Martin O'Leary was puffing and even Fred looked hot and damp-browed. They waved goodbye to Elsie and went downstairs and out onto Kiltie Street.

'Is that your cart?' Fred asked.

Annie shook her head. 'The cart man said he'd be back soon.'

'Very well. As long as it's gone within an hour or so.'

She watched him with his long sloping stride as he walked away out of Kiltie Street. She went back up to check on Davey. He was still sleeping peacefully. There was a clatter of noise in the hall and the bedroom door was pushed open. Paul stood there, a vein pulsing in his forehead.

'Where is it? What have you done?'

'Shh, you'll wake the baby.' Annie rose and motioned him out of the bedroom and gently closed the door.

They stood, face to face, in the hall. She felt the heat and rage radiating off him and was almost afraid. It's only Paul, she thought. Paul, with his twinkling dark eyes and careless charm and his ability to spin a yarn that had everyone laughing. Where was that man? She wondered wistfully.

'Well?' he shouted. 'Where's that bed?'

'I gave it away.'

'You what? I gave it to the cart man in part exchange for the new bed.'

Annie shrugged, trying to appear calm despite her trembling body. Paul wouldn't hurt her. She had to believe that.

'My friend needed a bed so I gave it to her.'

He raised his fist and she closed her eyes, waiting for the blow. When she opened them again, he'd gone. She couldn't believe it. Paul had never raised a hand to her before. She found herself shaking with the shock of it. That man wasn't her Paul. Her Paul had vanished the day he was taken off the battlefield, injured. Was this what she had to look forward to? When she was a child, growing up in Clydebank, there were women locally who appeared with black eyes or bruised jaws with weary regularity. Ivy had always tutted and shaken her head sympathetically but told Annie it was between a man and his wife and no one should interfere in that. Was Annie destined to be one of those poor women to be pitied?

A thin wail rose up from the bedroom, quickly turning to an outraged yell. Annie's own fists clenched for a brief second before she let out a shuddering breath and went to pick Davey up.

When he wouldn't quieten, she put him in the sling of her shawl and went outside again. The cart was gone. She jiggled Davey up and down, singing a lullaby but it made no difference. She walked along to the bench overlooking the grass area and sat down in despair.

–

Elsie said goodnight to Jessie with a smile. Her sister was now lying on a proper bed. Aunt Sarah had slipped into their room and given her pillows, sheets and a blanket.

'Don't tell Ada,' she said, slipping out again just as quietly.

It felt like a small victory.

'Aunt Sarah's on our side,' Jessie said.

'I think you're right. You can be the first to try our lovely new bed. Hop in and tell me what it's like.'

Jessie bounced on it and giggled. Elsie realised she'd almost forgotten what Jessie's laughter sounded like. It was good to hear it. She tucked Jessie in over her protests that she wasn't a wee girl any more. Feeling not at all tired, Elsie went out, intending to have a walk to the river or the canal. She spotted Annie's dark hair bent over her shawl and heard the baby yowling.

'Is he sick?' she asked, going over to the bench.

Annie looked up and Elsie saw the purple skin under her eyes. Poor girl, she's exhausted, she thought.

'I don't know what's wrong with him. He cries every evening for about three hours and then again in the middle of the night. My mother says it's normal and he's just colicky.'

'Would you like me to take him for a wee while and give you a rest?' Elsie said.

Annie pushed the baby at her gratefully. 'He's called Davey.'

Elsie took the hot, wriggling bundle and tried to rock him as she walked to and fro near the bench. The only experience she had of babies was when Jessie had been small but Ma hadn't let her help much. Still, it was a way of saying thank you to Annie for the bed. The walking and rocking weren't making a difference. Davey kept crying.

'You need gripe water,' a voice behind her said.

Turning round, Elsie saw a short, thin girl about her own age with mousey brown hair and thick glasses. Annie was staring, too.

'What's that?'

'Gripe water will fix the baby's colic. Is he your first?'

'He's not my baby. He's Annie's.' Elsie nodded towards the bench.

'I'm Doris. I live at number one. I was going out to put the scraps in the swill bin when I heard this wee person making itself known.'

'Do you know a lot about babies, then?' Annie said, coming over and taking Davey from Elsie.

'A bit. I grew up with lots of babies as neighbours and used to help out with them. You could try rubbing his tummy, too. That helps. The other thing is when you get home, take the sheet off your bed and swaddle him in it. That works.'

'I'll try that, thanks.' Annie held Davey in one arm and rubbed his tummy with her free hand. Soon, the crying subsided and he slept.

Doris looked pleased and Elsie found herself smiling at her and Annie.

'Peace and quiet reigns,' she said.

'For the moment,' Annie sighed. 'He'll be up again in the night. It's driving my husband mad.'

'Babies are hard work.' Doris nodded. 'It's worth it, though. He's a lovely wee baby.'

Annie's smile made her look suddenly younger as if her cares had fallen away for a moment. 'Did you say your name is Doris? I'm Annie and this is Elsie.'

Elsie felt drawn to the other two young women as they chatted quietly over the sleeping baby. Annie and Doris looked to be around the same age as her and it wasn't as if there were many young women living in the street so it was lovely to get to know them. It was only when the evening air cooled that they went back into the Kiltie Street flats, promising to meet up again. She was delighted to find out that Doris lived on the ground floor of the same tenement as her and she felt happier as she tiptoed into her room. Maybe she had found some friends.

# Chapter Six

'I'm sorry,' Paul said. 'I shouldn't have shouted at you and raised my fist. I'd never hit you, you know that, don't you?'

Annie nodded. It was the next afternoon and Paul had been out for most of the morning. She'd felt him slip into their contentious new bed last night and she'd pretended to be asleep even when his fingers touched her back. In the morning he'd been quiet and while she fed Davey, he'd gone off without a word. Now he was back but she knew better than to ask where he'd been.

'What do you say, we leave the wee man with his granny and I'll buy you a bun?'

Her first instinct was to think of the cost when they had a perfectly good biscuit tin with a few oddments still in it. Her second was to say yes.

'If Mum will let us, without constantly reminding me of her good deed.'

Paul winked. 'Leave her to me. You get ready for a treat.'

Sure enough, a half hour later they were trotting down the main street towards a local café. It felt good to just be herself with no baby wrapped to her and no tense muscles just waiting for the first cry. The sun warmed her face and she felt almost carefree until she saw the newspaper headlines, displayed outside the newsagent's shop. They screamed: *'Air-borne attack on Italy – then the West. Mr*

Churchill's assertion that there will be "*heavy fighting before the leaves of autumn fall*".' She glanced away. She didn't want to think of all those brave young men waiting to fight in Europe and take it back from the Nazis. Many of them would never see home again. Or they'd come back, like Paul, with limbs lost and minds altered by what they had witnessed.

Paul took her hand as they walked, only dropping it when they went inside the café and he ushered her into a chair at a small window table.

'What'll you have?' An elderly waitress came over with a pad and pencil.

'A couple of slices of your Dundee cake please, hen,' Paul said.

'I'll just warn you, it's no' the real thing but if you don't mind dried egg, powdered milk and a wee bit of oatmeal in your Dundee cake, then you'll be fine.'

She wrote their order in tiny, cramped handwriting on the sheet of the pad, which was already covered in writing. Paper was scarce these days.

'How did you persuade Mum to take Davey so we could go out?' Annie said.

'I'll give Ivy her due, she loves our wee boy so she snapped up the offer. I put it as if we were doing her the favour giving her time alone with the baby without us interfering.'

Annie laughed. Ivy complained that Paul was all charm and no substance but she fell for it all the same.

'Och, Annie, I've not heard you laugh in a long while and it's my fault. I can't seem to help it but I get these black moods on me and I cannae shift them.'

'I'm sorry too. I'm that busy with Davey, we never get a chance to talk any more.'

The cake arrived and Annie cut hers into small pieces to make it last. It was dry and slightly gritty but she ate it anyway. She glanced across at Paul who had made short work of his slice. He was wearing his dark blue jacket over a white shirt and black trousers. The left jacket arm was pinned up. He never asked her to help with the safety pins and she wondered how he managed. No doubt practice made perfect. Paul's silver badge glinted on his lapel and she saw the words 'For Loyal Service' on it. It showed everyone that he'd fought and done his bit. As if they couldn't work it out by looking at his arm.

'I know things are a bit tight at the moment,' Paul said, drumming the fingers of his right hand on the table.

An image of their new bed flashed before her eyes and she lowered them, hoping the words wouldn't spill out of her unbidden. The old bed had belonged to the previous tenants and she hadn't much liked it either, thinking of the possibility of bedbugs or fleas, but she'd have put up with the bed and made sure the rent could be paid.

'I've got a pal,' Paul was saying. 'Thinks he can get me some work.'

'Oh, that's marvellous,' Annie said, the relief making her feel weak. 'Thank God for that. Who is it? And what kind of work? Is it a garage? That would suit you fine, you being trained as a mechanic and all.'

Paul laughed, putting his hand up as if to ward off her flurry of questions. 'Hold your horses, Annie love. It's no' a full job I'm being offered.'

She waited impatiently while he turned his cup. Was he reading the tea leaves? When he didn't immediately speak, she couldn't help prompting him.

'Well, what is it then?' she asked. 'If it's not a proper job?'

He shrugged. 'A bit of this and a bit of that. It won't be a regular wage but Archie reckons he can pass enough work my way for us to be comfortable.'

'Is it all above board?' Annie's thoughts flashed briefly to Fred, the young policeman who'd helped lift the old bed into Elsie's home. They didn't need the law coming round to Kiltie Street.

'We'd better get back and give your mother a break from Davey. Don't want to take advantage of her good nature, do we now?'

Paul got up and offered Annie his arm and, pleased that he was getting along better with Ivy and in the chat with the waitress about the shortages as they paid and commiserated with her, she didn't realise until later that he hadn't answered her properly.

–

Doris woke up with a sore tummy and had a small asthma attack before breakfast which left her with no appetite.

'You're poorly, you should stay home,' Leila said, fussing around her.

Doris shook her head. 'I'm fine, Mum, and I can't let Franny down. She's finding it hard enough with only me to help.' The last word came out as a wheeze.

'What if you have another turn in the shop?' Leila sounded frightened.

Doris felt her nerves tingle and a feeling of slight panic in tune with her mother's. She took in a deep, steadying breath and was relieved to find that the wheeziness had passed. *I'm not afraid, I'm not.* It didn't help when Mum's imagination always painted the worst picture of what could happen. Then Doris's own imagination took flight and her worries bloomed.

Anyway, she knew fine well why she'd had some of her horrible asthma. It was Wednesday, her least favourite day of the week. The morning working at Franny's would be blighted by dread of the afternoon when she went to Mrs Mearns' flat where she was paid to clean the rooms and the stairwell. She was well paid though, so couldn't give it up.

'She's a snob,' Franny had said when she found out Doris worked for the Mearns. 'Only reason she has a cleaner is to show she's better than the neighbours.'

'Have you met her, then? Miss Mearns says her mother never leaves the flat.'

'I knew her when she was plain Isobel Smith. I sat next to her in primary school and she was no better than she ought to be. She acquired her airs and graces when she ensnared Arnold Mearns who had a few bob or two.'

'Ensnared?' Doris asked, fascinated in spite of herself.

Franny threw her an old-fashioned look. 'How does a girl marry a man who doesn't want to get wed?'

Doris frowned. 'I don't know. How does she?'

Franny sighed. 'You're a sweet girl, Doris, but my Lord, you've got a lot to learn.'

'I can't learn if you don't tell me.'

'Let's just say that Miss Ada Mearns was born early. Five months after the wedding, in fact.'

'Oh.'

'Yes. Once the ring was on her finger, Isobel stopped passing the time of day with us ordinary folks. She and Arnold were mixing with a better class and didn't she love to let us know that. When he died suddenly, she was left wealthy but the invites to the parties and gatherings withered away, or so I'm told. Other women are generally suspicious of widows and keep their husbands close.'

'That's sad,' Doris said.

Franny snorted rudely. 'She got what she deserved.'

Doris hurried to ask her questions before she lost Franny's attention. 'Is that when she moved back to Kiltie Street?'

'Aye, she came back with her children but she didn't take up any friendships again. She knew she'd burnt her boats on that. So, she went up into her five fancy rooms and stayed there.'

'The younger Miss Mearns comes into the shop. She's nice.'

'Sarah Mearns is a pleasant girl,' Franny agreed. 'Takes after her father. There was nothing wrong with Arnold except his taste in women. Now, enough of your chatter, go and get the mop and clean this floor.'

Doris had to be content with that although she was convinced there was more to the tale than what Franny had revealed. Why had Isobel Mearns come back to a street where she was hated? Wouldn't it make more sense, if you had the money, to move somewhere new and start afresh? As to why the old woman never left the flat, Doris couldn't imagine being a voluntary prisoner in your own home. She loved getting outside and dreamed of travel and adventure. Without Mum's fears infecting her, she was sure she could find her confidence. Not that she was likely to get any travel or adventure when the women's forces had all turned her down. Reading about the world in the newspapers, listening to the wireless and talking it over with Roy had to be enough.

That afternoon, after a quick dinner with Leila, Doris took her bucket and mop, scrubbing brush and yard brush and lugged them upstairs. She swept the stairwell and landing, polished the door brasses and was down on her knees with the red pipe clay drawing wavy lines to make a decorative border to the stairs when Ada Mearns opened the door to check on her.

'I'll be finished here in a moment and be right in to clean,' Doris said.

The door closed without a reply and she made a face at it. Then it occurred to her that Elsie might be home. She didn't know whether the other girl had a job or not, although if she was unmarried then it was likely she did some war work. For once, she didn't push open the door with a sinking feeling.

'Taking your time today, aren't you?' Ada commented sourly. 'Hurry along and dust in the parlour. Mrs Mearns is expecting you.'

Dusting the parlour was Doris's least favourite job. There were so many ornaments and knick-knacks that she lived in dread of knocking something over and breaking it. Mrs Mearns usually sat in the large armchair and watched her. That only made Doris more nervous and prone to clumsiness.

'Hello, Doris. How are you?' Sarah smiled as she went in.

'Fine, thank you, Miss Mearns. And yourself?'

'We're very well, aren't we, Mother?' Sarah said, putting down a hand of cards on a spindly table with a lace doily.

Mrs Mearns gave Doris a cold stare and didn't bother to reply. Doris dusted as quickly and as thoroughly as possible, knowing that the old woman would run a finger over the surfaces and call her back if even a trace of dust remained. She went out into the hall, wondering which room belonged to Elsie.

She pushed open the door to the adjacent room which she knew was Mr Leo Mearns' bedroom and was startled to see it was entirely bare except for a bed. The bare floorboards were dusty with remnants of carpet and a few carpet nails protruded.

'You can leave that room from now on. My brother has moved out and the new occupant will clean it herself,' Ada said, coming up behind her and making Doris jump. 'You can start with the kitchen. The floor needs scrubbing.'

Her hands hot with soapy water and the scrubbing brush moving over the shiny linoleum, Doris thought of that awful bare room and felt pity for Elsie. Why was she living here? Why had she no furniture? And why did Mrs Mearns and her two daughters not care about that?

She leant back on her heels and wiped her brow with a soapy hand. She wanted to help Elsie. She'd been so happy to meet her and Annie the other evening unexpectedly. It felt like they could become good friends. She didn't have many friends apart from Roy and his lovely family and Franny. Keeping company with Mum took up most of her spare time. Not that she had much of that, since she had three jobs. It had been lovely to chat to other girls the same age.

'I know what I can do,' she said out loud in the spotless kitchen. Whatever Ada Mearns' faults, being slipshod in her housework wasn't one of them and Doris only ever had to clean the floor in that room. 'Roy will help me, I know he will.'

Once the scrubbing, polishing and dusting was done to Ada's satisfaction, Doris made her escape downstairs. She didn't work Wednesdays at the factory and, eagerly, she put her cleaning materials away in the cupboard in their flat, anticipating her usual Wednesday evening activity.

First she made the evening meal and sat impatiently through it while Leila fretted about her lack of clothing coupons and tried to count up what a new housecoat would cost.

'I've got to go out,' Doris said finally, leaping up after a glance at the clock.

'Where on earth to? I don't like you going out in the evening, you know that. There are all sorts out there, ready to lure a young woman to a dark end. It's always Wednesdays you go out, did they ask you to clean at the factory again on an extra shift?'

'That's right,' Doris said, so used to her Wednesday lie that she didn't even blush. 'I won't be too long, though. I'll be back in time to listen to the music on the wireless with you.'

'All right, dear but do be careful. Why, only the other day, Mrs Lennox was telling me...'

Doris didn't wait to hear whatever doom and gloom was due. She slid her arms into her cardigan, flicked her fingers through her hair to plump it up and was gone. At the entrance to the close, she hesitated. Peering out with a furrowed brow, she waited until a figure emerged from number two and headed down Kiltie Street with a tuneful whistle and a cheerful greeting to anyone he met. When Roy turned the corner and was out of sight, Doris hurried to follow him.

She couldn't explain why she liked to do so. Partly it was because she wanted to keep him safe and it felt like if she watched him until he turned in at the warehouses then she could breathe a sigh of relief. Mostly it was because she loved him so much and, watching his slightly sloping walk, his forward-thrust shoulders, his tousled dark hair, made her tingle with wanting him. She'd watch him until he reached the warehouses and then she'd sit for a while, watching and imagining him inside doing his job. She only did it on a Wednesday. Surely one evening a week couldn't hurt? And no one had to know, did they? It was her little secret. One she hugged happily to herself.

Only, today was going to be different. She had to talk to him about her idea for Elsie. She allowed herself the pleasure of watching him until the warehouses came into view up on the canal bank. Their blackened stonework and small windows looked grimy and depressing in spite of the summer evening.

Before he reached the warehouses, she ran to catch him up.

'Hey, Dor. What are you doing here?' Roy grinned in surprise.

'I came to ask you something.'

'You'll have to make it quick or old Hugh will be out to find me. I'm on in five.'

'I know but this can't wait.'

'What is it?' Roy frowned in concern. 'Everything all right with you and your Ma?'

Doris nodded. She loved that he cared so much about her. Mind you, he was like that with all the neighbours. She tried to focus on her thoughts instead of his firmly shaped lips and just the hint of dark bristles on his jaw. He wasn't much taller than her but he had an air of strength about him.

'I've got this friend, Elsie. She's moved into Mrs Mearns' flat on the top floor above us. Only, she's got no furniture except a bed.'

'If she's only moved in, perhaps her furniture has still to make the move,' Roy said.

'I get the feeling she has none. I was wondering…'

'The salvage?' Roy grinned. 'Of course you can take some.'

'Can I?' Doris brightened. 'Oh, Roy, you're wonderful. You guessed what I meant before I even said it. Are you sure? You've spent a lot of time doing up those tables and chairs.'

'Look, I've got to go now or old Hugh will be on the warpath, but come round the yard tomorrow and I'll have looked some stuff out for you.'

A bulky figure had emerged from one of the warehouse entrances and was waving. Roy and Doris waved back.

'You'd better go or Hugh will be over here blaming me for making you late,' Doris said. 'Thanks, Roy. I'll see you tomorrow.'

She almost skipped back home. Roy worked at Stevenson's salvage yard during the day and he took broken pieces of wood and metal and made them into useful items. Some of those were sold on by the salvage merchant but Roy was allowed to keep any he wanted as part payment. Not that he did, he'd told Doris. It wasn't as if there was room at his home for any of it.

It was worth it to see the look on Elsie's face the next evening when, between them, they carried up the stone steps a table and two chairs and a small, battered sideboard to the top floor of number one.

Ada Mearns answered the door and looked at them as if they were unwanted salesmen.

'Good evening, Miss Mearns. Is Elsie home?' Doris asked politely.

'Elsie?' Ada said, as if she'd never heard of her.

Doris began to think she'd got it wrong and that Elsie lived a floor down but then she saw her in the hallway behind Ada Mearns, smiling at her.

'Hello, Doris. How nice to see you. Will you come in? Is that all right, Aunt Ada, if I invite my friend inside?'

Ada Mearns looked stunned but didn't have time to speak before Elsie had waved Doris and Roy inside.

'This is my pal, Roy. We brought you some furniture. I… I noticed you didn't have much when I was cleaning here on Wednesday.'

'It's not much, mind,' Roy said, 'But you're welcome to it, hen. If you like.'

'If I like… it's grand. You did this for me?' Elsie said.

There was a glint of tears in her eyes and Doris looked away hastily in case Elsie cried. Then Roy chuckled and she heard Elsie laugh shakily too. Trust Roy to ease the mood.

'Come on then, help me pull this lot in,' Roy said, cheerfully.

Between them, they got the furniture into Elsie's sparse room. There was a younger girl sitting on the bed, reading a book. She jumped up when they came in.

'This is my wee sister, Jessie,' Elsie said. 'Look what Doris and Roy have given us.'

'Do we have to pay for them?' Jessie asked.

'No, hen. It's a gift,' Roy said gently. 'See, these bits of wood were all broken up and no one wanted them. They were going for firewood but I can fix things up so I made these and I wanted them to go to a nice home. So here we are. What do you think?'

'You're very clever,' Jessie announced once she'd inspected the table and chairs and pulled open all the drawers in the sideboard.

They all laughed and Doris felt like hugging them all. Oh, it was so nice to be part of something and to be in a wee group with friends.

'Will you stay for a drink?' Elsie said. 'I've got my own supplies now. Or rather, my Aunt Ada has let me have my ration's worth.'

Doris was bursting to ask why she hadn't had any furniture and how she got along with the strange Mearns family but she held her tongue. She was only just getting to know Elsie. Maybe once their friendship was deeper, she'd ask.

–

Annie found herself humming the tune of 'My Bonnie Lies Over the Ocean' as she went round her home, putting things in their place and hanging clean washing on the pulley before raising it up to the kitchen ceiling and tying the cord in place. It wasn't her turn for the copper she shared in the back yard with the rest of the tenement so she'd handwashed her underwear and some of Davey's tiny clothes. Davey was sound asleep in his makeshift cot and Paul was out at the pub, having promised he wouldn't be long.

She smiled as she thought about their recent trip to the café. Here she was humming when she could've burst out loud in song if that wouldn't wake the baby. She hadn't felt this happy since... well, she couldn't remember. Paul had apologised for his behaviour, held her hand as they walked along and, best of all, had found some work. She had decided not to ask too much about what it was until he was settled into it. Not only that, she'd met Elsie and Doris who seemed so friendly and nice and had been kind to Davey. She didn't feel quite so alone.

Annie was so deep in her pleasant musings that at first she didn't hear the noises from the street. When she registered the shouting, there was already a hammering on her door. She hurried to open it, afraid Davey would wake. Paul almost fell onto her and she was hit by a waft of beery breath.

'Are you drunk?' she cried, as he swayed, bloodshot eyes trying to focus on her. 'Paul, you promised...'

'One bloody drink, that's all,' he slurred, putting his hand out.

She wasn't sure if he was trying to touch her or steady himself. He staggered forward and with a shock she saw there was someone else behind him in the close. It was Fred Cooper, his dark blue uniform smart but the sight of it sending fear shooting through her.

'What's he done?' she said, holding on to Paul's waist as if she could keep him upright.

'Please don't be worried, Mrs Thom. Your husband was causing a bit of a disturbance down at the King's Arms so I thought it best to bring him home.'

'Are you charging him?'

'Not if he stays home and gets some sleep,' Fred said.

Paul staggered sideways and Annie lost her grip on him. He crashed down on his knees, sending their umbrella stand flying. Annie ran to help him up.

'Leave me be, why can't you!' he yelled, arms flailing. 'Bloody well leave me be, all of you.'

His one good arm, milling around, struck her on the mouth and she cried out in pain, stumbling back. Touching her bruised lips, her fingers came away red with bright blood.

'That's enough,' Fred said, moving past her swiftly and dragging Paul to his feet. 'You're coming with me. A night in the cells will cool you down.'

He had Paul's arm in a firm lock. Annie's mouth was sore and her lip was swelling but she still felt the shame of it all and a shaft of sadness and pity for Paul.

'What will happen now?' she asked.

'He'll be let go in the morning,' Fred said. 'You can come and collect him. Are you going to be all right? That lip looks nasty.'

Annie nodded. 'It's nothing. He didn't mean it, you know. He's drunk and he lashed out but he didn't mean to hit me.'

Paul's eyes were shut and he didn't appear to hear her or Fred. He mumbled to himself and a tear squeezed from his eyelashes. Suddenly she couldn't bear it any more.

'Take him away please, Constable Cooper. I'll be there tomorrow.'

She shut the door on them both. Her lips stung and there was a coppery taste of blood in her mouth. How would they live this down? Everyone must've heard the noise and there'd be no mistaking the sight of Paul Thom being manhandled down Kiltie Street by the police. She dreaded their pity or worse, the gossip there'd surely be.

# Chapter Seven

Fred Cooper and his parents lived in one of a row of cottages built for the railway workers at the turn of the century. The Marymore cottages were low with slate roofs and roses and ivy growing around the front doors. Fred loved the sounds and sights of the nearby railway and the broad, brown flow of the river. Occasionally the river water changed colour due to the factories pouring out their waste into it. Tonight, his walk home was slow after a long day at the shipyard followed by a shift with the police.

'I'm home,' he called, as usual, as he ducked his head to get into the tiny hallway.

'Have a good day, son?' Bert said, coming out to greet him.

'A quiet one, thank goodness,' Fred said, taking off his cap and rubbing his head. 'That you away out?'

Bert had his Home Guard uniform on and his rifle was leant against the wall. His tin hat and gas mask were on the floor beside it.

'Yes, we're training tonight. Bit of marching and how to stick Jerry with our bayonets. Lovely. Your mum's away out on a couple of visits. She's left your tea in the oven to keep warm. See you later, son.'

Fred went into his room and changed out of his uniform, making sure to hang it up so there would be no creases. He was proud of it and knew that he was 'doing his bit' like everyone else. It was tiring, working all day at the shipyard, coming home for his tea and then heading out again for a shift as a special constable but he had no complaints. Everybody was tired and working too hard. He even covered some day shifts when his hours allowed at the yard.

He took the slice of vegetable pie and a small glass of milk over to the kitchen table and tucked in. His thoughts turned back to work. It had been quiet lately, a few drunken brawls the most exciting events. Which reminded him of Annie Thom. He should have booked her husband for being 'drunk and incapable' with a summons in due course after the incident a few weeks ago. He'd put him in a cell with a mattress and blanket and checked on him in case he choked on his own vomit. But in the morning he had let Paul Thom go with only a warning. And that was because of Annie. Her face had been white as she came to collect her husband. She had her baby with her and she looked so vulnerable he could barely stand it.

He stared at the last forkful of pie and turned it slowly on the plate. It wasn't right, thinking of another man's wife like he did about Annie. He admired her spirit. She took care of her child while dealing with a drunken brute for a husband. He was taken with her gleaming black hair the day they had moved the bed. She and Elsie had been cheerful and eager to help lift it and no complaints.

Fred sighed and swallowed the last of the pie before scraping his plate clean. He had to see her again to make sure she was coping. He'd turn in to Kiltie Street tomorrow on his beat. It couldn't harm, could it now?

About the same time that Fred was finishing the pie, Paul Thom was sauntering up the steep road above Kiltie Street to the street with the large houses sheltered by trees. Reaching the top, he stopped to catch his breath. There were views to the distant Campsies and Kilpatrick Hills, a world away from the city. He turned back to the houses and went to the one at the end of the street where Archie lived. He could have picked it out even if he didn't know where his old pal lived. The other houses were shabby and war-weary but Archie's, well, that was something else. No one had cared about his house in a very long while. He couldn't imagine Archie caring enough to paint the walls or even wash the windows. They were blacked out upstairs and he stared at them, wondering what was hidden inside the rooms.

'You took your time answering,' Paul said, when the front door finally opened.

'Never mind that, get inside quickly.'

'You've done all right for yourself then.' Paul nodded as he looked about the spacious hall. It was dark and a smell of damp pervaded the air but it was a big place, no doubt about it. There were good, solid doors leading off the hall and a wide staircase to the floor above.

'It was my wife's.'

'I didn't know you were married.'

Archie laughed sourly. 'Aye, there's a lot you don't know about me and don't need to. She's dead now anyway and good riddance to her. Best thing she did was leave this place to me.'

He gestured for Paul to follow him and they went into a room that held a large dining table and chairs and not much else.

'Not one for decorating?' Paul said mildly.

'Let's get something clear right now.' Archie leaned his bulky stomach against the back of one of the chairs. 'We might be old pals but this is business. So, let's skip the pleasantries, shall we, and move on to why you are here. Sit.'

Paul sat. Archie sat opposite, scratching his greasy hair as if in thought.

'I was hearing from various folk that you need a job. So, I've a proposition for you.'

'It's no secret that I'm out of work,' Paul said. 'Annie wants me to get a job in a garage. I was a mechanic before the war.'

'Do you want to hear ma proposition? I'm no' interested in what you did before.'

'All I'm saying is, I need a proper job.'

'Do you always do what your old lady says?' Archie jeered. 'Treat her the way I did mine and give her a wallop when she opens her mouth. That'll learn her good.'

'What are you offering?' Paul said, stung by Archie's words.

He wasn't henpecked and he might listen to Annie but he didn't have to do what she said.

'I need someone I can trust. A right hand man, if you like. And I see you've been unlucky with the left hand but you've still got your right.' Archie grinned nastily.

Paul clenched his one good hand under the table but bit down on a response. Planting his remaining fist in Archie's pudgy face would be satisfying but he needed this job, whatever it was.

'I'm listening,' he said.

'It's a bit of this and a bit of that. If I send word, you come running. There's packages will need moved, messages taken and sometimes I need a look-out man. It's not regular hours but it'll pay you well. What do you say?'

Paul was no stranger to breaking the rules. He and his brothers had poached game for years, growing up in Clydebank near the countryside. Later, he'd bought and sold goods without asking their provenance. A younger Archie had often supplied items off the back of a lorry to the lads that hung around town. But for a moment, he wondered what he was getting into. Then he thought about Annie's reproachful face when he went to the pub and the way they had to ask Ivy for the rent money and he nodded.

'Aye, I'll do it. When do I start?'

'That's the ticket. And as a gesture of goodwill, come and choose a wee something for yer wifey from my store.'

He led the way to another room. With a flourish, he unlocked it. There was a wooden counter across the entrance and he lifted the hatch and went inside with Paul following. The space was stacked with tins and packets and bottles.

'Help yourself,' Archie said. 'There's Spam and tins of peaches, bottles of beer and I've got bars of soap. What's wifey's name again?'

'Annie,' Paul said, trying to ignore Archie's derisory tone.

He had to make this work; they needed the money. God forbid that Annie found out what the job was, though. He knew she'd like the soap but how could he explain where he got it from? He took a couple of tins of Spam and a tin of peaches. It'd be hard enough getting away with that.

'Tell Annie it was a gift from your old pal,' Archie suggested with a grin. 'That's no lie.'

Paul slid the tins into his jacket pockets.

He was out onto the street when Archie shouted after him, 'I'll be in touch. You be ready, mind.'

—

Elsie was drying plates in the kitchen when Aunt Sarah came in. Aunt Ada had announced that she was going for a well-deserved nap and wasn't to be disturbed. Quietly, Sarah picked up a cloth, picked up a plate and began to dry it.

'You don't have to do that,' Elsie protested. 'I can manage fine.'

'If we all help each other, it makes the chores lighter.' Sarah smiled.

If only Aunt Ada shared that sentiment, Elsie thought wryly. Her older aunt was very quick to give out orders and tasks to both the girls. There was a comfortable silence for a few minutes with only the hum of the range and the gentle clink of the dishes as they worked together. Sarah gave a little cough.

'I hope I'm not being nosey but... I wondered if Louise... your mother...' Sarah put down the tea towel and Elsie saw her swallow before she went on. 'If she was happy?'

Elsie thought about the drinking and the days when Ma would bemoan their lack of money and claim wildly that no one cared about her, that she could die and it wouldn't matter at all. She suppressed those memories. They weren't for sharing. Instead, she conjured up the images of Ma laughing and singing. Oh, how she had loved music. A terrible, helpless desire to see her mother once again rippled through her and she had to turn away for a moment to compose herself.

'She loved to sing and dance,' Elsie said eventually. 'And she loved Jessie and me.'

Aunt Sarah nodded, a small smile curving her mouth, and Elsie was glad she had given her that.

'Were you close as children?' she asked, putting the last plate away and turning to her aunt.

'We were a rare taggle, the lot of us,' Sarah said, her face brightening as she stared past Elsie, remembering. 'Mother was a disciplinarian but when we had a chance, we ran wild. The games we played, such imagination. Father encouraged us; he said it was good to be creative but we knew to knuckle down when Mother found us.'

It was nice to hear Aunt Sarah chuckle and Elsie wanted to hear more. Especially stories about Ma growing up. Grandmother called querulously from the parlour and, with a gentle touch to Elsie's shoulder, Sarah hurried away. Elsie found herself smiling at what Sarah had told her, imagining Ma as a wee girl playing with her sisters and having a rare time. She dried her hands and folded the towel neatly so that Aunt Ada wouldn't scold her later.

—

'Why do you have to go out?' Jessie whined.

'I told you. It's the knitting club night. I won't be that long and anyway, you'll be asleep so you won't miss me.' Elsie sat on the bed and stroked her sister's hair back before planting a kiss on her forehead.

Jessie yawned and turned her head away into the pillow. Her muffled voice came up, still unhappy. 'You're always out in the evenings, I never see you.'

'That's not true. I've got late night shifts Tuesday and Wednesday nights at the factory and Doris has set up our wee knitting group for Thursdays but apart from that I'm here.'

'I don't like being alone.'

'Och, you're not alone,' Elsie said, losing patience at last. 'You're a big girl now, Jessie and there's three other people in the flat. Now, if you need anything, you just nip out and ask Aunt Sarah, all right?'

Jessie's large eyes looked reproachfully at her but she nodded and slid down under the coverlet. Elsie sighed and reached out her hands but stopped and put them into her pockets instead. Was she wrong to keep her sister with her? Perhaps she should take her back to Perth but Elsie couldn't bear the thought of them being parted again. It was selfish, she knew, but with Ma gone, she needed her sister with her – even if Jessie had to learn that Elsie couldn't be there all the time for her. Besides, Elsie needed something enjoyable in between working at Fearnmore, doing housework for Aunt Ada and worrying about her sister. Doris's knitting club had met twice and she looked forward to it.

'I love knitting and, as they say, "If you can knit you can do your bit",' Doris had said, when she suggested to Elsie and Annie that they join her one evening. 'We can have our own wee knitting club and make jumpers, balaclavas and socks for the forces. What do you think?'

Elsie had leapt at the chance to deepen her friendship with the other two girls. Annie had hesitated until Doris told her that Davey was very welcome. Elsie suspected that she didn't want to ask her husband to look after the baby. From things Annie let slip, it appeared as if he wasn't the most reliable man.

'We can knit for Davey too,' Doris suggested, 'if we can get some pretty wool.'

The smell of damp wool hit her as Doris let her into the ground floor flat. Annie was sitting in the kitchen, an unravelled old jersey on the table beside her, stretching the wool onto long, twelve-inch cards. A black kettle was boiling on the range and Elsie could almost feel her hair curling in the steamy atmosphere.

'It's a bit much, isn't it?' Doris laughed, taking off her spectacles and wiping the lenses. 'It's fogging up my specs. I'll take the kettle off the heat now. We're just getting some new wool carded from a jersey I've outgrown.'

'Where's your mum tonight?' Elsie asked.

At their last two get-togethers, Leila had taken Davey into the kitchen to keep an eye on him while the girls took over the parlour with their bags of wool and knitting needles and a pot of tea. Elsie had noticed how relieved Annie was that Doris's mother seemed to dote on the baby and his cries quickly settled with her. A bottle of gripe water was handed over but he was restless and Leila kept him on her lap to jiggle.

'She's away out to see a friend 'cos she's that worried about the call-up. You'll have seen it in the papers; they're calling it the "grannies call-up". Women aged forty-six up to fifty have to register for war work and my mum has turned forty-six so now she's terrified she'll be sent into the army.'

'They wouldn't do that, would they?' Elsie asked, intrigued and slightly appalled.

Doris shook her head. 'I don't suppose so but it's fraying my nerves listening to her fret about it all the day. Perhaps her friend will have an idea what they can do. Annie's disappointed she's not here to keep Davey but, to be honest, I'm quite glad to have the peace and quiet.'

'She should open a nursery; she's so good with Davey,' Annie joked.

'That's not a bad idea,' Doris said. 'You might have hit the nail on the head. After all, there's plenty of younger women struggling with war work and cooking and shopping and looking after their kids. Not all of them will have family willing to help out.'

'Or their family's all working too,' Elsie said. 'I'm glad Jessie's old enough that I don't need to be there for her, even if she thinks I'm neglecting her as it is. Your mum could make a real difference.'

'If the bombers come back, would she get the children to safety or would her nerves give out?' Doris mused.

'Well, there hasn't been any bombing since March when Jerry dropped incendiaries on Govanhill and destroyed the Queen's Park church.'

'Aye, that was a shame, that was.'

'Let's hope and pray that Hitler has his eyes elsewhere,' Annie chipped in, putting her wool cards down and stretching her back. 'The poor souls in Europe are getting it in the neck but that'll keep him busy and away from Glasgow.'

'What about you?' Elsie asked, 'Don't you want to be evacuated? You've got a baby so you're eligible.'

Annie shook her head. 'I can't leave Paul. I've thought about it and maybe if the bombers return I'll change my mind but right now, no. I'm needed here.'

Elsie didn't like to ask more. Annie had told them last week that Paul had a job and seemed pleased. Why then was she needed here? Wasn't it more important to protect Davey by taking him to the countryside? But she still didn't know Annie well enough to probe further. She did wonder if everything was all right between Annie and her husband. She'd had a split lip a while ago but told them she'd bumped into the baffle wall.

They went into the parlour and got out their knitting. Soon the comforting sound of clacking needles filled the cosy room. Doris muttered under her breath. Elsie smiled as she glanced over at her. Doris had pushed her thick spectacles up onto her head and had her knitting up close to her face, counting stitches. She had lovely big brown eyes, Elsie thought. What a pity they were behind glass all the time. Beside her on the couch, Annie was frowning at her woollen sock. She had admitted she wasn't a natural knitter but she was keen to be involved. Balls of Sirdar Air Force Blue wool bounced beside them as they worked and the war knitting patterns were placed on the carpet.

'Did the WVS centre give you more khaki and navy wool?' she asked.

'Yes, Mrs Woodley weighed it out for me. She apologised but they weigh the garments when we hand them in so they know if any gets nicked. It's getting harder to get other colours of wool,' Doris said, looking up. 'If we had other nice colours we could knit for Davey and ourselves and for people who've been bombed out or evacuated.'

'It's tough now wool's on ration,' Annie agreed, putting her half-finished sock on her lap and looking at them both. 'I've unravelled all the old jumpers I've got.'

'We need more but where can we get it?' Doris said.

'I know where there's a lot but I don't know how we get it,' Elsie said.

'Tell us then, you've got us hooked,' Doris cried.

With Doris and Annie both staring at her, Elsie felt self-conscious. 'My Aunt Ada's got me doing housework in the evenings that I'm in the flat, dusting and polishing and the like. I was tidying a cupboard in the hall and I came across shelves stocked with balls of wool – all sorts of lovely colours and some that would do for army and navy woollens. It must all be a pre-war stash.'

Doris clapped her hands. 'That's perfect.'

'Not so fast,' Elsie said, taking in a breath to fortify herself. 'My grandmother's never going to give it to me. She's... she's not like that. I asked Aunt Sarah and she said none of them knit now. Grandmother and Aunt Ada have arthritis in their fingers and Aunt Sarah doesn't have time as she's at Grandmother's beck and call.'

'Oh, what a pity,' Doris's shoulders slumped. 'Never mind, we'll just have to find some jumble sales and have a rummage. Problem is that half the girls in Maryhill will be doing the same.'

'Don't be so quick to give up,' Annie said. 'Maybe there's a way... Elsie, does your grandmother like a bargain?'

'I don't believe she likes anything. She just sits in her parlour all day. But Aunt Ada likes a bargain – or rather likes to get one up on everyone. Why?'

'What if there was a way to exchange that wool for something else, like an ornament or a jar of jam, say?'

'Ooh, you mean a Bring and Buy sale?' Doris squealed excitedly. 'What a great idea.'

'That might work,' Elsie said, feeling excited too. 'We get the wool and Aunt Ada gets... well, whatever someone else contributes. We can raise money for soldiers' comforts. Or we could do a salvage drive?'

'That's usually metal or bones. And there's no call for a Spitfire Fund any more either. No, it's got to be a Bring and Buy for comforts. We can have it in the street and we'll need to contact the police for permission,' Annie said. 'Who's going to organise it? I can help but I've got my hands full with Davey.'

Davey began to cry as if to agree and, with a long-suffering sigh, Annie lifted him from his blanket on the floor and rocked him back and forth. Elsie looked at Doris.

'It has to be you, Doris. If I organise it, I bet my aunts won't come and we need that wool.'

'Och, I couldn't,' Doris said nervously, 'I'm too shy to ask folk.'

'Yes, you can,' Elsie and Annie chorused together. 'You can, Doris, and we'll help you.'

# Chapter Eight

Doris was over at Roy's home on a Saturday afternoon. Roy's mum was away shopping and the younger Allens were outside running about and making lots of noise in the street. They waved to her and she waved back. She used to help look after them when they were babies. Nan Allen, who was now working at Bishopton, was the same age as her and they'd been firm pals. Nan was awful fond of her big brother, Roy, and so the three of them had hung out together over the years and found they had a lot in common.

With Nan living out near the Royal Ordnance Factory, Doris and Roy had continued their friendship. Some might find it odd that a young woman and man could be just friends but she didn't care what they thought.

Jock Allen winked at her as she came in. 'Back again, Doris, hen? Soon you'll be asking for your own seat. Fancy a rocker like mine?'

'Don't tease her, Grandad. She's brought the papers and if you're good, Doris will read the headlines out to us.'

Doris had come for Roy's advice on the Bring and Buy sale but her thirst for knowledge diverted her onto the state of the war.

'There's lots happening. Give me a moment and I'll spread the papers out and tell you,' she said eagerly.

Roy cleared the table and moved his grandfather's rocker closer so the old man could hear. Doris shoved her spectacles up onto her hair and moved her finger over the newspaper print.

'"*Rome prays after great Air Armada attack*",' she read out. 'And it says: "*Riots follow one thousand tons blow at Milan*".'

'That's the Americans and the RAF heavy bombers inflicting that,' Roy said with pride and a hint of envy.

Doris glanced up at him. She felt for him. She knew he wanted to be in the thick of it, fighting for his country.

'What else, Dor?' he grinned.

She peered at the newsprint. 'Randazzo captured. It says that Randazzo, key to all German positions in Sicily has been captured by Allied troops. And here's another column all about some place called Kharkov. Says fighting in Kharkov and on to Smolensk, the Red Army has broken through the enemy defences in a double-armed blow south of Vee… Vaa… Vyazma. They don't half make the place names impossible to pronounce!'

Roy looked as pleased as if he'd personally organised the forces' victories.

'Didn't catch the last part,' Jock Allen said loudly. 'Read it again, hen.'

'It's all right, Grandad. We're winning, that's what's important. I bet you it won't be long before Italy surrenders.'

'Do you really think so?' Doris said.

'Aye, I do. Stands to reason, if you look at the news recently. They haven't got a snowflake's chance in hell, if you'll pardon my French.'

'No swearing in front of a lady,' Jock said sternly. 'Your ma won't stand for it.'

Doris laughed as Roy looked sheepish. 'I can handle it, Mr Allen. Thanks very much, though, for calling me a lady. I like that.'

'Cup of tea, Grandad? That way I can put your rocking chair back in its usual place and me and Doris can get some peace.'

'Cheeky young bugger,' Jock muttered, forgetting the rule about not swearing in front of ladies. 'Och well, yes, I will have a cuppa, then.'

'I'll put the kettle on,' Doris said, leaping up and then grimacing.

'What've you done to your leg?' Roy frowned.

'It's nothing really. Did I tell you about our neighbour, Mr Gibb, and how he's frightened Mum so she won't go into the back court?'

'You mentioned it.'

'She's got me going out there to water the veg and the flowers. I went down there this morning and he's only gone and pulled out some of mum's pansies that had strayed over the invisible line and put them in a pile on our side. They're all wilted and dead.'

'He sounds odd,' Roy frowned deeper. 'What about your leg?'

'I fell going back up the steps. You know me, I'm that clumsy. It's just a bruise and I'll mend.'

The tea was made and poured and Roy pushed his grandfather's rocking chair back to the cosiness of the range with a mug to hand.

'I cannae imagine what secrets you and young Doris have got that I cannae share,' Jock said, winking at Doris.

She flushed but Roy rolled his eyes and grinned before joining her at the table. Before long, Jock's gentle snoring began and when Doris looked back, his head was tilted up, his mouth open and his eyes shut tight.

'You should tell that Mr Gibb to mind his own business,' Roy said, picking up the conversation again.

'Oh, I couldn't. I'd be scared to.'

'You've got to stand up for yourself.'

'Anyway, I came to get your advice,' Doris said hastily.

It was no good Roy telling her to stand up to Mr Gibb. She was far too timid to do so. It didn't help that her mum kept suggesting what their strange neighbour might do next. Doris's imagination had exploded with awful possibilities. She tried to put it all out of her mind and explained to Roy about the knitting club and their lack of wool and their brilliant solution.

'So, you see, I've agreed to organise a Bring and Buy sale but I'm getting anxious. My nails are all bitten down. I wish I hadn't said I'd do it.'

'People don't have much these days and what they have, they hoard. Will anyone have enough to give at a sale?' Roy looked doubtful.

'We never thought of that. You're right, it's a terrible idea.' Doris's heart sank.

'I never said that. You've got to have faith in yourself, Dor. It could be the way to get your hands on that wool. How do you know the Mearns will bring the wool? They could bring anything. From your descriptions of their home, it sounds like they've got ornaments and all sorts to sell or swap, unlike most folk.'

'Elsie's confided in her Aunt Sarah, who's promised to persuade her sister to offer the wool. The other Miss Mearns likes china ornaments and pretty plates so if we can find a few to bring to the sale, we might just get what we want.'

'I'll help where I can. Hugh's got a couple of trestle tables we can borrow. I'll ask him tonight. And I've got a couple of battered table tops I can rustle up on wooden legs for the event.'

'Thanks, Roy, you're a pal. I'm still nervous, though.'

'You've no reason to be. You're the cleverest girl I know, so if you can't organise a Bring and Buy then I don't know who could.'

Doris puffed a little with pride. It would be lovely if Roy also said she was the prettiest girl he knew but, as that was unlikely, she'd have to accept being clever.

Elsie had dusted the headboard and legs of her bed, her table and two chairs and the top of her sideboard with pride and pleasure. How kind Doris and Roy were to have brought her the furniture. She'd nearly bawled her eyes out at their thoughtfulness. Now she was sitting at the table, making a small rag rug for the bare floor. There was no way she could afford a proper carpet or linoleum but a couple of cheerful, brightly coloured rag rugs would make all the difference.

A quiet knock at her door made her put down the half-finished rug and go to see who it was. Her Aunt Sarah stood there, smiling.

'Ada's gone out to queue for meat and veg for this evening's meal and Mother is asleep. I thought you and I could have a chinwag.'

'Jessie's out in the close so I'd be delighted.' Elsie smiled back.

Aunt Sarah had proved to be a real friend and comfort in an otherwise cheerless, unloving atmosphere. Elsie was used to Aunt Ada's sour face and snippy comments by now, and that her meals and Jessie's were small with the tiniest portions grudgingly given and their meat mostly gristle while Ada and Isobel had the choicest parts and Sarah's meals were somewhere in between in quality and size. There was certainly a pecking order in the cold Mearns' flat. Sometimes, Elsie could hardly bear it but she knew she had to keep up a pretence of happiness for Jessie's sake.

Elsie followed her Aunt Sarah through to the spotless kitchen. Ada kept it shipshape and poor Doris scrubbed it well on Wednesdays. She'd asked Aunt Sarah why they paid for Doris to come when Aunt Ada cleaned every other day and was told it was all about keeping up with appearances. Isobel Mearns was a cut above all the neighbours and wanted everyone to know it.

'If she's so wealthy, why does she live in Kiltie Street?' Elsie had asked, genuinely confused.

'I believe it's because of your mother, my sister Louise; that she wanted to be near her,' Aunt Sarah had said sadly. 'For all her faults, my mother is capable of love and Louise was always her favourite. At least until...'

'Until what?' Elsie asked, but Sarah shook her head and said that was for another day.

Remembering that conversation and knowing there was no one else in the flat, Elsie was determined that 'another day' might as well be this day. She waited until Sarah had bustled about clearing the table of crockery before speaking.

'Aunt Sarah, you were going to tell me more about my ma.'

Sarah's eyes flickered nervously to the door.

'We'll hear her coming back,' Elsie reassured her. 'And we'll hear Grandmother calling you when she wakes up.'

Sarah nodded. She didn't look happy though, as she poured the tea and fussed with the saucers.

'Please…' Elsie prompted.

'Very well. You have a right to know, of course. It's just hard to speak about Louise. I can't believe she's gone. She was the youngest girl, you know. I was six when she was born and she was the prettiest of us girls. Such beautiful golden curls and violet eyes… but of course she knew it too and used to toss her hair and flutter her eyelashes as she grew up.'

'Ma was eighteen when she had me. I remember her saying that.'

'That's right. She was married to Michael at eighteen and you came along nine months later. He wasn't much older. By then of course I had expected to be married myself.' Sarah's voice broke.

'What happened?' Elsie asked, laying her hand over her aunt's for comfort. 'Only don't tell me if it's too painful.'

Sarah shook her head. 'Gracious, I ought to be over it by now but somehow I don't believe I ever will be. My fiancé was killed in the Great War at the Battle of the Somme. I've never wished to marry anyone else. Larry was the love of my life.'

'That's so sad. I'm sorry for your loss,' Elsie said.

'Ada says I should snap out of it. That I've mourned long enough.'

'Did Aunt Ada lose her man then, too?'

A whole generation of men had been lost in the Great War and everyone knew of maiden aunts and spinsters amongst the community.

'No man was good enough for Ada. She had an offer once but turned him down because he was too poor and his mother was cheap, or so Ada thought. No one else asked.'

Elsie wasn't surprised. Who'd want a bride with a sour face and nasty disposition? She didn't want to talk about Aunt Ada. She wanted to know about Ma.

'Michael was my dad,' Elsie prompted.

'Yes, of course. He was a nice man, very quiet while Louise was bubbly and funny. I thought them a strange match but at first it worked.'

'But later?'

Aunt Sarah shifted in her chair and looked uncomfortable. 'I don't know if I should be telling you too much. Mother won't like it.'

'Please, if you don't tell me then no one will. All I know is that he died when I was young. I have no memories of him so he must've left when I was wee but then there's Jessie so Ma must've been seeing him somewhere at that time. There were no photographs of him in our home and Ma wouldn't talk about him.'

'Very well. I'll tell you what I know, which is very little. One day, Louise came here with you. She was very upset but would only speak to Mother. Ada, Leo and I were told to make ourselves scarce. When we were allowed back in, Louise had gone and Mother told us she wasn't welcome any more and that we were not to mention her name in the house, ever.'

'Is that all you know?' Elsie cried, feeling so disappointed.

Sarah nodded. 'I'm sorry I can't be of more help. I was so curious to know what had happened that I went along to Louise's flat when Mother didn't know I was out but Louise slammed the door in my face and shouted that she didn't want anything to do with any of the Mearns ever again. I never dared to go back.'

Elsie thought how like Ma that was. She'd always taken powerful emotional moods, up and down, and let her heart rule her head. *Oh Ma! Now,* Elsie would never find out about her father or what had gone on.

'You must have seen Ma and my father on Kiltie Street after that,' she persisted.

'Yes, a few times and then I never saw Michael after that. I think he passed away. That was the rumour, anyway.'

A slamming door somewhere downstairs made them both jump. Elsie laughed shakily.

'Aunt Ada won't be back for a while the way the queues are. She had me queuing the other day for fish and it took me an hour to get to the end only to find there was none but they were selling tins of Spam instead.'

'And a very nice meal it made too.' Sarah smiled but her fingers, woven together, showed her nerves were taut.

It's ridiculous the way we're on edge because of two spiteful old women, Elsie thought ruefully.

'Leo and his new wife, Alice, are coming for a meal this evening. That's why Ada is being extra careful with finding ingredients. She's very fond of Leo. He's the baby of the family, although of course he's forty-one.'

'He married late, then.'

'We thought he'd remain a bachelor so it was quite a shock when he brought Alice home to meet us. She's quite a bit younger than him. You'll meet them soon enough. Mother said to tell you to be sure to wear your best clothes, Jessie too.'

–

Leo and Alice Mearns arrived a little after six that evening. It was a warm August evening and Ada had opened the windows to let the air in. A smell of sulphur from the factories made her close them again and Elsie blotted the sweat from her forehead with a little of the precious powder from her compact.

'Who are the people coming to tea?' Jessie asked, tugging at her skirt which was getting too short.

'It's our Uncle Leo and his wife, Alice,' Elsie said, brushing her hair. 'Grandmother wants us on our best behaviour. Och, Jessie, stop with the stretching, you'll tear that material, it's so thin. We don't have the coupons for a new skirt.'

'Can you ask Mrs Woodley if there's any clothes at the centre? She said I could have some as I was growing so tall.'

'Did she? When was that?' Elsie said, smoothing her own dress and feeling unaccountably nervous.

She was annoyed with herself. There was no reason for them to want to impress Uncle Leo or the new Mrs Alice Mearns. She took a calming breath. They only had to be polite for an evening. That was all.

'I saw her in the street a few days ago. She was dressed in her lovely green costume and I told her I liked her hat. It's green as well and has a maroon ribbon.'

'Aye, that's the WVS uniform. It's very smart. I wish I had that instead of a boiler suit and a turban for work.' Elsie grinned.

'So, can I choose some clothes from the centre?'

'Let's worry about that later. I hear voices. I think they've arrived. Come on, Jessie. Let's go and meet them.'

Leo and Alice Mearns were icily polite when introduced to Elsie and Jessie by Isobel. Ada had prepared a sausage pie with slices of tomato on top and new potatoes, although there was no butter and only a skim of margarine to help them slip down. For dessert she'd made an apple tart and a jug of thin custard. Elsie had to admit Ada had made an effort for her brother and his wife but they hardly said thank you for the meal.

The conversation was of Leo's important job as a guard on the railways. Isobel's stern face even broke into a small smile as she informed Elsie and Jessie of their uncle's invaluable work to keep the railways running. Alice, dressed in a yellow costume far too old for her, kept her gaze on Leo and copied him, seemingly unconscious of the fact that she did so. If Leo took a sip of water, then she did too. When he straightened his shoulders while telling them facts about the trains, her small shoulders lifted too.

When Elsie's gaze caught hers, Alice swiftly looked away. The couple did not ask any questions about Elsie or Jessie, nor was the subject of Louise's death brought up or any condolences offered. Elsie was tiring of hearing how marvellous Leo was at his job when her grandmother spoke again.

'Take Jessie to your room now. It's time for her to go to bed and for you to entertain yourself.'

Elsie took the hint. She might think it very rude to be dismissed so readily but in truth she was relieved to get away from them all. Aunt Sarah looked sympathetic and Elsie gave her a little smile to show she wasn't upset. She herded Jessie from the table and, as they went through to their room, she heard them all getting up and going into the parlour.

'It's too early for me to sleep,' Jessie complained, jumping up onto the bed and flinging herself about restlessly.

'I know but we'll have to stay in here at least until Leo and Alice have gone.'

'I didn't like them much. He's got cold eyes like Aunt Ada and she's got thin lips that are pursed up like this.'

Jessie demonstrated by pressing her lips together and Elsie gave a giggle. She really did have the look of Alice down perfectly.

'You mustn't do that, it's cheeky,' she said.

'You laughed.'

'I know but I shouldn't have, not really. You mustn't cheek your elders.'

'I don't think you liked them either,' Jessie huffed. 'Don't lie and say you did.'

'We haven't had time to get to know them so I can't say whether I do like them or not. Listen, why don't you get undressed and get your nightie on and I'll go and heat up a mug of milk for you.'

Jessie nodded and Elsie crept quietly from the room, knowing that the kitchen was empty. She couldn't help tiptoeing to the parlour door and leaning her ear in to the voices within. Then she wished she hadn't as Leo's pompous tones sounded.

'Why have you taken those two in, Mother? They're not your responsibility. Louise made her bed and had to lie in it.'

Then Isobel's voice. 'It's my Christian duty. I can't see her children destitute.'

'You were always soft on her, even when we were children. You should have washed your hands of her when she was careless enough to lose her husband.'

Ada then chipped in. 'That's enough, Leo. Mother has done what she considers to be right. We don't like them and we're not spoiling them but they have a roof over their heads and are learning to be grateful for that.'

Elsie pressed her fingers to her mouth to stop a cry coming out. They certainly weren't being spoiled by kindness. It was only too obvious what a burden they were to Grandmother and Aunt Ada. If it wasn't for Aunt Sarah's friendship, she didn't know how they'd survive in this house.

'I'd like to see them gone. I won't be happy knowing they're here but Alice and I will keep visiting to make sure they're not taking advantage of you,' Leo said.

There was a creak in the floorboards as if someone was walking towards the parlour door and Elsie dashed silently into the kitchen, her heart thudding. She waited but no one appeared. Furious with them all, she heated the milk and poured it into a mug, taking it back to her room for Jessie.

'There you are, love. Are you going to read your book?'

'I don't have my book. Grandmother took it.'

'What do you mean, she took it? Why would she do that?' Elsie gasped.

'She said I was being naughty and talking back to her but I wasn't. She had me cleaning the brasses and I was tired after school and I had homework and you were out at your knitting club and I said I wouldn't do the brasses any more. She slapped my face and took my book as a punishment.'

'You never told me.'

'I'm telling you now, aren't I?' Jessie hunched up on the bed and cupped the mug in her hands, blowing on the milk to cool it.

Elsie felt a rage soaring up into her. How dared their grandmother punish Jessie? She was minded to storm right into the parlour there and then and demand the book back. She was almost at her door when she realised it would be better to wait until Leo and Alice had gone. Otherwise, they'd say that was exactly why Isobel shouldn't give them a place to stay.

Jessie was asleep by the time Elsie heard the good-byes in the hall. She waited a while longer and then walked briskly across to the parlour. Aunt Ada passed her, carrying a tray with empty plates. Elsie stepped inside. Her grandmother was sitting in her usual armchair and there was no sign of Aunt Sarah. For a moment, she caught a glimpse of Ma's features on the old woman's face but, as Isobel frowned, it disappeared, leaving her with a strange, bittersweet feeling.

'What do you want?' Isobel said coldly.

'I want Jessie's book back. You had no right to take it,' Elsie replied.

'The girl was rude and insolent. She had to be punished.'

'She was tired after a day of school and had her home-work to do. Instead, you made her polish brasses.'

'I'd like to remind you that you are both here on charity. I could just as easily throw you out.'

Isobel's hands gripped the armchair and Elsie saw the swollen, red joints. She felt a sudden, unwilling, sympathy for her grandmother, thinking how painful her fingers must be.

'It's a poor sort of charity when you slap a wee girl's face,' Elsie retorted.

A dull red stained Isobel's neck and she didn't answer for a moment, but then she nodded. 'Very well, I'll return the book.'

She pushed herself from the armchair. Elsie stepped forward to help but the glare she received made her stop. With a stiff, dignified walk, Isobel went to the sideboard and took the book from the top drawer. She made to hand it over but as Elsie went to take it she held it still.

'You look like your mother but you're more like him.'

'Like my father? I'd be proud to be like him. I only wish I had known him before he passed away to find that out.'

Isobel Mearns' expression changed from haughty coldness to surprise. 'She told you he'd passed away?' She sat back in her armchair with a dry, humourless chuckle. 'Louise was always such a liar. So, she lied about that too, did she?'

She looked up at Elsie, who was standing there, unable to move. 'Your father's alive and living in Glasgow.'

# Chapter Nine

There were nappies everywhere. They were steeping in buckets on the kitchen floor and boiling on the range and she'd hung some of them up on a line in the back court to dry in the hot sunshine. Annie wiped her forehead with the effort. The smell in the flat was none too good. Davey was gurning in the other room and Ivy was in there settling him. For what felt like the hundredth time, Annie felt a flicker of resentment towards him. If only she'd not got caught so quickly after getting wed. She'd only ever wanted Paul. If she was honest, she hadn't thought of babies. It was a shock to find herself pregnant immediately and then Paul was gone, off to war, leaving her uncertain and scared.

Ivy appeared with a red-faced Davey, snot dribbling down his chin.

'Feed him, will you? He's a hungry wee mite.'

'I fed him an hour ago,' Annie protested.

Ivy's brows rose. 'It doesn't matter. I fed you and Brian as you demanded. Babies don't have a clock, now, do they?'

With a heavy sigh, Annie unbuttoned her blouse and grabbed Davey, plugging him on and wishing she was elsewhere.

'What's got into you? You're sullen all the while,' Ivy said.

'I've no time to myself. None at all. I'm either feeding the baby or washing his clothes or cleaning up the house.'

Ivy sniffed. 'That's what marriage is, love. It's hard work and no praise. Your reward is a contented husband and a healthy wee boy. So, stop complaining and get on with it.'

Davey snuffled against her and Annie was ashamed. She did love him, really. If only it wasn't all so... difficult. Sometimes she felt so alone. She'd tried to tell Paul how she felt but she knew he wasn't listening. He'd kissed her cheek and promised to take her out somewhere soon. She didn't want to go out; she was so exhausted. She just wanted him to understand.

'Your lip's healed. No more walking into baffle walls then?' Ivy said.

'No, I'm all right.'

Annie knew fine well that Ivy suspected Paul had hit her. She wasn't going to satisfy her mother's curiosity by admitting it. Ivy would love to have that to hold against him.

'That's my lad asleep. Give him here and I'll pop him in his cot. Then I'm away up the road to see wee Mrs Connelly.'

'Doris's mum?' Annie was surprised. 'How do you know her?'

Ivy took the sleeping Davey and rocked him gently on her large, soft bosom.

'I met her on the street and we got chatting. It turns out she wants to join the WVS so I said I'd go round and fill her in on all the activities we do. Then I'll head home from there. You've got your messages and I've left you a pudding.'

'Thanks, Mum. It's kind of you.'

Ivy sniffed again but Annie could tell she was pleased. 'Aye, well, it's a milk pudding with a handful of raisins soaked into it. You're too pale, you need feeding up. I don't expect that husband of yours has noticed. Too busy being down the pub.'

'Actually, Paul's got a job,' Annie said. She hadn't mentioned it before to Ivy because it was such odd hours that it didn't seem like a proper job. Lately, though, he was out all day and every day.

'That so? What is it? I hope it's a decent job in a garage, fixing cars. That's what he's trained for, is it not?'

'He's working for a friend, doing heavy lifting and some clerking.'

'You won't need me to help you out with the rent money any more then, or buy your messages. I don't mind helping out, love, but it leaves me a bit short, so it does.'

Annie didn't want to say that so far Paul hadn't given her much extra money. He had produced a few tins of food instead on a regular basis. She nodded.

'We'll manage now he's working,' she said, and hoped it was true.

She saw Ivy out the door once Davey was in his cot and then sank down on the bed for a rest. She'd hardly closed her eyes when there was a sharp rap at the door. Thinking Ivy had forgotten something, she hurried to open it.

'In the name of the wee man, that's a braw stench you've got in there, hen.' A man with thinning brown hair and a sizeable paunch over his belt grimaced before walking in without being invited.

'Well, well, so this is Paul's wee hoose and you must be his lovely wife, Annie. I'm Archie Bale, an old pal of Paul's. Is he in?'

126

Annie's mouth still hung open while her visitor looked in both rooms before turning back to her in the tiny hall.

'I forgot you had a babbie. It doesnae take a detective to work that out with all them nappies hanging everywhere but I saw the babbie too, sleeping like a bug.'

'Sorry, who did you say you are?' Annie said, trying to take control.

How dared he saunter into their house as if he owned it!

He grinned, showing yellow teeth and a gap where one was missing. 'I told you who I am. Shall we have a wee seat and a nice chat?'

She shivered when he touched her arm but forced herself not to show that she found him disturbing.

'I'll have beer unless you've got something stronger,' he said, sitting down in Paul's chair as if he owned the place.

'We don't have any beer or wine. I can fill you a glass of water.' She lifted the pot of nappies and set it aside before taking a glass and putting it under the tap.

Archie drummed his fingers on the kitchen table. When she turned, he was watching her. There was a prickle between her shoulder blades when she turned back to the sink and she hurried with the water.

'You know yer man's working for me now,' Archie said behind her. 'You should be grateful.'

'Oh, I didn't realise... sorry, I didn't know you were Paul's new boss.'

She set the full glass down on the table as steadily as she could under his unsettling gaze.

'Aye, that I am. So are you?'

'Am I what?' Annie said, confused.

'Grateful.' He took a slurp of water and looked her up and down.

'We're both glad that Paul has found work,' Annie said primly.

Her fingers touched the front of her blouse, wondering if she'd left a button undone from feeding Davey. His muddy brown eyes followed her hands. They were the colour of the clay in the canal sides, she thought. The clay never smelt good and neither did he. Even with the powerful odour of the boiled nappies, a whiff of sour sweat reached her nostrils.

'Oh, he's working, all right. Making himself indispensable, so he is. Did you enjoy the Spam and peaches?'

So that was where Paul had got the tins. This repulsive man had given them to him. If he brought more, would she eat them, knowing now where they came from?

'Yes, they were very nice. Thank you,' she forced herself to say, wishing he'd just go.

'There's plenty more where those came from if Paul works hard.'

'Mr Bale, I don't want to be rude but my baby's going to wake up soon and I've got my housework to do.' Annie got up from the table but his hand came down on top of hers and clamped it to the wood.

'There's no need to be so hasty now, is there? We're just having a nice, wee conversation you and I. I think you'd want to be nice to Paul's boss, seeing as I'm paying your rent and putting the food on your table, so to speak.'

She pulled free, at once angry and frightened. 'I want you to leave now.'

Archie Bale leaned back in his chair and laughed. 'A feisty woman. I like that.'

Annie skirted the table, aiming for the door but he got up out of his chair and grabbed her waist.

'I'll scream,' she cried.

'What for? I'm here leaving a message for Paul, that's all. You don't want him to lose his job, do you? Who else is going to employ a cripple?'

The fight went out of her and she sagged in his grasp. He lifted her chin and she recoiled from his bad breath. He kissed her on the mouth and pushed her back against the wall. Annie's heart pounded in fear. Then he let her go.

'It's been nice to meet you, Mrs Thom. I'll call again some time soon. Let Paul know I was looking for him. I've got another wee job needs done.'

When he'd gone, she ran a cloth under the cold tap and scrubbed her lips until they stung. She thought she was going to throw up but it passed. She ran into the bedroom and picked Davey up. He wriggled in his sleep but she cradled him close and kissed his soft, downy head until the sweet, milky smell of him calmed her. I'll tell Paul, she thought. He'll have words with that man, make him sorry he ever came here. But she knew, even as she fixed it in her mind, that she couldn't. Paul needed the work. They both did.

She'd barely settled Davey when there was another knock at the door. Slowly, she picked up the coal shovel and went to open it. Fred Cooper stood there, the silver badge and black and white band on his peaked cap glinting in the sunlight, his boots highly polished and his uniform looking crisp and neat. He raised an eyebrow at the sight of the shovel. Annie looked at it.

'I was just… I'm tidying up. Is there something the matter?' Her mind flitted to Paul and then to Archie Bale.

'Nothing the matter,' Fred said, taking off his cap and ruffling his blond hair. 'I thought I'd check on you. May I come in, Mrs Thom?'

'Yes, of course. Excuse my manners. Come away in, but quietly, the baby's asleep.'

Annie put the coal shovel back in its place in the kitchen and tucked a stray strand of hair behind her ear. Here was her opportunity. She could tell the friendly policeman about what had happened. He'd arrest Archie Bale and she'd be safe.

'Are you quite all right? You look pale, forgive me for saying it,' Fred said, looking concerned.

Annie managed a shaky laugh. 'That's you and my mum both saying that today. But I'm fine, really I am.'

'I'm on duty, Mrs Thom, so I'd better not linger too long. How's Mr Thom?'

'He's not come back drunk and milled his fists into my mouth again, if that's what you mean,' Annie said drily.

Fred blushed and she saw how young he was. Not much older than herself probably. Paul's two younger brothers, about Fred's age, were in the army somewhere in Italy. He sometimes got a rare letter from one of them. There were very few young men about who were not in uniform – except the shipyard workers, of course. And Fred was clearly doing his bit being a special constable. She wondered what his reserved occupation was.

'That's good, that's good.' He seemed to run out of things to say and Annie waited, unsure what he wanted. At least she had the coal shovel if he was anything like her last visitor.

'Well, I'd best be off,' he straightened his shoulders and smiled down at her. 'If you need me, you know where to find me.'

'Thank you,' she said, knowing she wouldn't tell him about Archie Bale's advances any more than she'd tell him about her suspicions about Paul's work which kept him out late evenings and sometimes overnight.

When he left, she felt helpless and more alone than ever.

–

Elsie walked purposefully across George Square which was right in the centre of Glasgow. She had arranged to meet Fred Cooper on his day off and wanted to be away from Kiltie Street and the curious gaze of any neighbours. She didn't want her grandmother or Aunt Ada finding out and asking her what she was up to. In the few weeks since Isobel had let drop the shattering news that her father was still alive, she'd been unable to find out more. Isobel simply refused to speak to her on the matter. Aunt Sarah had been just as shocked as Elsie when she told her. Between the long hours at the munitions factory, shopping for food, cleaning the house and caring for Jessie there had been no time or energy left to think about what to do.

Leo and Alice Mearns came every Sunday for dinner, making it plain that they disliked Elsie and Jessie. Leo had taken Elsie aside on one occasion as Aunt Sarah and Alice took Isobel into the parlour after the meal to settle her into her armchair, and Aunt Ada took the plates into the kitchen.

'We're watching you,' he told her coldly. 'You're taking advantage of my mother's good nature by living here and eating her food.'

'Grandmother asked us to come and stay, and we've got our ration books,' Elsie said.

Leo made a noise deep down in his throat as if it was caught with phlegm. 'I can see through you even if she can't. I want you and your brat of a sister out of here.'

'We aren't going anywhere,' she said bravely although her heart was thudding at the confrontation and the palms of her hands were damp. 'We've nowhere else to go.'

'That, my dear, is not my problem. It might take a while but I can promise you, I will get you out.'

Aunt Sarah came out of the parlour at that moment and asked Leo to come and join his mother and wife. She gave Elsie a little smile but hurried back into the parlour. Elsie knew she wasn't expected to join them. Aunt Ada beckoned her from the kitchen and she was almost glad. She'd much rather spend the evening scrubbing the pots and plates than sit in a room with people who appeared to hate her. Jessie was already putting the scraps into the food bucket under Ada's instruction. It was getting harder to put a bright face on to shield her from the unpleasant atmosphere but Elsie knew she had to try.

She grieved for Ma when her mood was dark as it was now. She finally understood why Ma had lied and said she had no family. Being in their stingy embrace, barely tolerated and treated unkindly, Elsie realised that their mother was only trying to protect her girls. What would Ma think now if she knew her daughters were being so cruelly used because of her rebellion? As she washed the dishes, her mind was on how they could escape from Kiltie Street.

George Square and the surrounding magnificent buildings, like the rest of Glasgow, showed the changes wrought by the war. There were sandbags across entrances and the buildings' tall windows were criss-crossed by tape in case of bomb blast. The crowd thronging the area included large numbers of young men and women in forces uniforms. The familiar stone lions and statues were untouched but now there was a brick and concrete air raid shelter in the square. A workman was busy checking its door. The white paint defining the door and edges was supposed to make it visible in the blackout but the paint was so grubby that Elsie wondered if it made any difference. The posters, half peeled from the brick, called on her to 'Be Like Dad and Keep Mum' and to 'Hasten the Day' by taking out war bonds.

She remembered walking through the square back in May when Ma was still alive. It had been Wings for Victory Week and she'd gone especially to see the launch. It was magnificent and the event would stick in her memory forever. The Polish Army Choir had sung from the steps of the city chambers, beautiful rousing songs that seemed to go right into her bones. Then Lady MacRobert had released over a thousand pigeons from the roof of the grand city chambers. Elsie had overheard someone in the crowd saying that each pigeon was meant to represent ten thousand pounds of the city's target. The newspapers later reported that Glasgow had exceeded its target and raised over sixteen million pounds by fund-raising, a sum of money so large Elsie couldn't get her head round it.

Today she passed a single Polish airman feeding the pigeons and didn't have the heart to tell him it was forbidden to give bread to animals. He smiled at her and she smiled back but hurried on. There was a café on a side street off the square and she didn't want to be late to meet Fred. She was hoping he could help her.

Fred was sitting at a small corner table and he stood up politely as Elsie came in. He looked smart and oh-so-handsome in dark trousers, a matching jacket and white shirt.

'Thank you for meeting me on your day off,' she said, a little flustered as she met his clear, green gaze.

'I'm very glad you gave me an excuse to get out of the house. My mum needs heavy lifting done,' he grinned.

'Oh, what will she do?'

'Don't worry, I'll do it when I get back. My stepdad's back isn't up to it.'

She realised he'd been teasing and felt daft. He was a nice man; of course he'd help his mum. She'd been around Uncle Leo too often recently and forgotten that not everyone was like the Mearns family. The waitress came and they ordered Camp Coffee and shortbread.

'What can I help you with?' Fred asked, breaking his small finger of shortbread into two.

The sweet chicory scent of the Camp Coffee hung in the air between them. Elsie took a bite of her own shortbread before she answered. It was important to get it right. 'I've got a problem and I wasn't sure how to solve it but then I thought maybe you could give me some advice.'

Fred nodded encouragingly and suddenly Elsie found herself telling him the whole sorry story. About how she and Jessie had ended up in the top flat at number one Kiltie Street, how they weren't wanted, Uncle Leo's threat and, more than anything, the fact that her father wasn't dead. 'So,' she finished breathlessly, 'how do I go about finding him?'

'Firstly, I'm sorry for your troubles,' Fred said. 'None of this can be easy for you.'

She kept her gaze on the shortbread and crumbs on the plate in front of her, afraid that if she looked at his sympathetic face, she'd burst out crying.

'The thing is, Elsie, this isn't a police matter. Your father, Michael Weir, isn't a missing person. He's alive and living in Glasgow, according to your grandmother. We've no reason to believe otherwise.'

'But why has he never been in contact with me? Why have I never known him at all? He must have been around because Jessie was born eleven years after me.'

Fred shook his head. 'Perhaps he left and then came back?'

'But I would've seen him then. Unless it was a short-lived affair the second time around.' She blushed. It was a bit awkward talking about Ma's love life with a young man she hardly knew. But Fred didn't appear to be embarrassed. He was frowning over the puzzle.

'The only way to be sure is to find your father and ask him. Which takes us round in a circle. How can you find him? You're certain if you ask your grandmother she won't answer you?'

'I've tried, believe me. She clams up and won't speak to me. My Aunt Sarah didn't know Michael was alive; she was told he died.'

'What about your other aunt?'

'Aunt Ada wouldn't help me if I was on fire,' Elsie said. 'I'm not even going to try asking her.'

Fred took a good, long sip of his Camp Coffee. She noticed how his Adam's apple moved on his neck and the golden bristles that had escaped the razor on his jaw before she looked away, her nerves tingling.

'Are there any papers in your mum's belongings?' Fred said. 'Her marriage certificate, for example. I don't know how much that would help but it'd be a start. Or there could be letters between them, that sort of thing.'

Elsie sat up straighter. 'Ma had a box with all the certificates and important papers – in case of bombs, you know. We used to take it into the shelter with us when the raids were on, along with our gas masks and a flask of tea.'

'That's the one.' Fred grinned. 'That's where you start.'

'It's no good,' Elsie groaned, 'Grandmother took it for safekeeping when we moved in. She'll never give it back now. She'll know why I want it.'

'It belongs to you so you've a right to have it. Wait until there's a quiet moment and go and look for it, if you want my advice.'

'Rummage in the flat, you mean, through Grandmother's room?' Elsie took in a sharp breath and her shoulders tensed as if she was already committing the deed.

Fred laughed. 'Maybe as a policeman I shouldn't suggest that. But if it was me, wanting answers, then that's what I'd do.'

Could she do it? She'd be scared of being found out but she had to give it a go.

'Thanks, Fred. You've been a big help. Must be that policeman's job; your head's screwed on right.' Elsie smiled.

'I'm glad someone appreciates it,' he said with a wry grin.

'What do you mean?'

'I don't know if you've noticed but most policemen in Maryhill these days are older. Most men my age have joined up, like Tam McRae who I've never met but keep getting told it's his post I've filled. He's a local hero.'

'Do you want to join up? I thought you must be in a reserved occupation if you're a special constable?'

Fred's sigh shook his whole body. Elsie wanted to reach over and hug him but of course she couldn't give in to that impulse.

'I'm a riveter at the shipyard which is reserved but I'd enlist like a shot if I could. Oh, folk don't come right out and say it – or most of them don't – but it's there, a question in their eyes. I'm a young, able-bodied man so why am I still here? Particularly when their son or nephew or brother is away fighting.'

'Your jobs are essential. If every shipyard worker and policeman up and went to the Front, there'd be mayhem. I remember when the bombs dropped on Maryhill a couple of years ago; there were policemen right in there digging people out of the rubble and organising ambulances and stopping the looting. We'd not be safe without the likes of you, Fred.' Elsie leaned forward earnestly to get her message across.

'Thank you, you're a good listener,' Fred said with a smile.

'And so are you. I feel an awful lot better getting all that about my grandmother and my father off my chest.'

They sat smiling foolishly at each other and Elsie felt she could drown in the green pools of his eyes. Before she made a complete idiot of herself, she broke the strange trance by saying brightly, 'Oh, that reminds me. My friend Doris told me to ask you about this Bring and Buy sale we're wanting to organise. Only, she reckons we need police permission to hold it on Kiltie Street.'

'She's right but I can easily get permission for you. Not only that, I'll donate some stuff for the sale. What are you raising the money for?'

They chatted as Fred paid for the coffee and shortbread and then they walked out onto the pavement. Fred said he had a few errands to run in the city centre and Elsie didn't want to outstay her welcome so she was quick to say she needed to get back home. She waved to him as he strode off on long legs. Then, with renewed vigour, she headed for the tram. She had to find Ma's papers. Surely within them there must be a clue as to where her father was.

# Chapter Ten

It was a dull, rainy evening at the start of September but inside the ground floor flat at number one, Kiltie Street, the knitting club was taking place in the snug parlour as the girls clicked their needles and frowned over the patterns which were slowly becoming familiar. Leila had taken Davey into the kitchen and they heard her singing 'Bye, Baby Bunting' and Davey's answering coos and gurgles.

'I need your help,' Elsie announced, putting down her half-knitted balaclava.

Annie and Doris looked at her expectantly. Elsie bit her lower lip as she decided how much to share of her family story but, gazing at their kind faces, she knew she had to simply tell the truth. She realised they had become her two best friends and friends shouldn't keep secrets from each other. The other two girls stopped their knitting too as she explained about Louise's death and the discovery that she and Jessie had a grandmother, aunts and an uncle and, finally, that her father was alive.

'That explains a lot,' Doris said, when she stopped for breath. 'I wondered how you'd ended up living with Mrs Mearns and why your bedroom was so bare. What horrible people they are.'

'Not Aunt Sarah,' Elsie said quickly. 'She's been a comfort and a help. If it wasn't for her, I don't know how we could stay strong.'

'So, now you need to get your hands on your ma's box of papers,' Annie said.

'Yes. Only I don't know how, when Grandmother never leaves the flat and Aunt Ada only leaves to go to her Red Cross meetings and that's during the day when I'm at the factory. If I'm off on weekends, Aunt Ada seems to always be there and I swear she keeps a beady eye on me. She certainly keeps me busy, washing and cleaning – and then Uncle Leo and his wife come most Sundays.' She sighed with frustration.

Doris paced the small parlour floor until she tripped on a wrinkle in the rug and came to a stop. 'I've got it. There is a way for you to get the papers while Miss Mearns is fully occupied.'

'Tell me,' Elsie begged, sitting forward eagerly and squashing the balaclava.

'It's simple. You'll get them during the Bring and Buy sale this Saturday coming. You told us Miss Mearns likes a bargain and she'll come along for ornaments and plates. That's your chance to look in the flat.'

'Oh, but I'm helping you at the sale. I can't be in two places at once.'

'Me and Annie can hold the fort for a wee while and you can nip up and be back before anyone's noticed.'

Annie nodded. 'Doris is right. It's the perfect time to do it.'

'Not if Grandmother's awake.'

'Then you'll have to ask your Aunt Sarah to suggest a nap or at least keep her busy in the parlour so you can dash into her bedroom,' Doris said.

Elsie nodded. 'I know you're right but I can't help feeling a bit nervous. What if I get caught?'

'I'd be terrified,' Doris admitted with a weak grin. 'But that's just me. I'm a scaredy-cat. You're not like that. You're stronger than me, so you are. Isn't she, Annie?'

Annie nodded. 'You can do this. You have to do it if you want to find your father.'

Trust Annie to put it plainly. Elsie's heart beat a little faster even at the thought of sneaking into her grandmother's bedroom and hunting for Ma's box. But it had to be done, otherwise she'd never know. Somehow, not knowing was the worst.

'What will you do if his address isn't there?' Annie asked.

She hadn't thought of that. It stopped her short and she felt as if all her breath had left her. 'Fred thinks it must be.'

'Fred Cooper? You spoke to him about it?' Annie said, sounding surprised.

Elsie nodded. She was so caught up with the idea of finding nothing in Ma's box that she didn't notice Annie watching her.

'Of course it'll be there,' Doris said, nudging Annie. 'Of course it will.'

'I was just...'

'It's all right, Doris. Annie's right. I have to be realistic. I don't know if I'll find him but I've got to try.' She picked up her knitting again. One purl, one plain and repeat. The comforting pattern kept her thoughts at bay.

Annie hadn't taken up her own knitting. She plucked at the ball of wool until her almost completed scarf began to unravel. Finally, she spoke. 'If we're having an evening of confidences, can I be next?'

'If you'll put down that scarf, you can,' Doris said. 'What's the matter?'

Annie put the scarf and knitting needles down on the sofa beside her. 'I don't know how to start.'

'We're your friends. We're here to help you,' Elsie said gently. 'Just start at the beginning.'

Annie's eyes glistened but she didn't cry. She took a breath that lifted her shoulders as if to fortify herself and then described the visit that Archie Bale had made where he'd kissed her. Elsie and Doris listened in horror. Annie's head lowered.

'I feel so ashamed, as if maybe it was my fault he kissed me. I couldn't tell Paul.'

Doris sprang from her armchair and ran over to put her arms around Annie, hugging her fiercely. Elsie got up and sat on the sofa beside her, touching her arm to bring comfort. Now the tears trickled down Annie's face and she sniffed until Doris passed her handkerchief over.

'It wasn't your fault at all,' Doris said. She looked at Elsie for help.

'You mustn't blame yourself,' Elsie said. 'He's a disgusting pig, taking advantage of you. Has he been back?'

Annie blew her nose and straightened her back. 'Twice he's been back, always when he knows Paul's on an errand for him. He hasn't tried to kiss me again but he struts round our flat like he owns it and he… brushes against me, knowing I hate it but I can't do anything about it. If I complain, he'll sack Paul. We need the money Paul brings in. His pension isn't enough, what with Davey and all. Forget I said anything, please. There's nothing that can be done.'

There was a subdued silence for a moment. Even the singing in the kitchen had stopped and Elsie guessed that Davey must have fallen asleep. Doris's mum would be holding him in her arms. She'd told Annie that she'd spent hours like that when Doris was a baby, holding her close and she loved doing it again with Davey.

'Does he turn up unexpectedly or would you know when he'll call again?' Doris asked.

'The last time he sent a message with Paul to say that he'd be dropping off a package and I was to be there to take it. I know he did that to wind me up but I had to nod and tell Paul that I'd take the package in for him. He was chuffed as if I'd made him proud. He's so much happier these days, I can't bear to bring his mood down.'

'Let us know next time he wants to drop a package off,' Doris said.

They took up their knitting again, subdued by Annie's tale. The rain hurled itself against the tenement window and a sudden breeze rattled the glass pane.

'I hope it's better weather on Saturday,' Doris shivered. 'It's like bloomin' winter tonight.'

'Even if it's raining, we'll go ahead with it. We're not made of sugar, as my mum would say,' Annie said, seeming glad of a change of subject.

'What else do we need to do for the Bring and Buy?' Elsie asked.

She knew that Doris had worked hard to find trestle tables and to ask the neighbours to bring their old china and things they didn't need any more to help their good cause. She and Annie had helped put up flyers on the lamp posts and baffle walls advertising the event. Fred had come good with the permission to hold the sale in the street and promised he'd be there on the day. It gave her a warm glow thinking of seeing him again so soon.

'There's not much left to organise. But Mum thinks I've bitten off more than I can chew,' Doris said. 'She's worried it's going to be a disaster and it'll be all my doing.'

'And what do you think?' Elsie said. Leila Connelly might be a nice lady and very good with Annie's baby, but it made her angry, the way she undermined Doris by projecting her own fears. Mrs Connelly was so nervous of everything and it infected Doris too as she was so close to her mum.

'Och, I… I don't know, to be honest. Maybe it will be a disaster.'

'That's ridiculous. It's going to be great and you've done a fabulous job organising it,' Elsie said firmly. 'Hasn't she, Annie?'

'It all seems in hand,' Annie agreed. 'It would be hard to mess up a Bring and Buy sale.'

Elsie winced inwardly. *Oh, Annie!* Sometimes, Elsie had a desire to shake her for her blunt manner. Luckily, Doris looked a bit happier. She pushed her specs back up onto her head and picked up her knitting.

'Come on, girls. Let's get another few rows done before we call it a night. I can't wait to get my hands on all that lovely wool from the sale.'

–

'It is raining,' Doris wailed as she opened the blackout curtains on Saturday morning.

'I knew this was too much for you. Why did you agree to do it?' Leila said, shaking her head as she put the porridge bowls on the kitchen table.

'I want to do it, Mum. It's not too much for me. At least… I don't think so,' Doris said. 'Why can't you be glad for me?'

Leila's worried frown was almost more than Doris could bear, her nerves were that jangly. 'I am glad for you, love. But I'm your mum, it's my job to protect you. And there are so many dangers out there. Especially now there's a war on.'

'I just wish you could be less… overprotective. I'm twenty, Mum. If I get married, I won't be here and I'll have to make a go of things, won't I?'

'I can't bear the thought of you leaving me,' Leila fretted. 'I do try, Doris, I do. But I can't help being anxious.'

'I know, Mum, but it rubs off on me. Like all that business with Mr Gibb. I've been avoiding him.'

'And so you should. He's very odd. It's the way he looks at me.'

'Well, it's all right to look, I suppose, as long as that's all he does.' Doris leapt up.

'Where are you going? You've not had your breakfast.'

'I'm away to Roy's. I'll eat after.'

Roy's home was a bustle of bodies as the Allen family got ready for the day. Doris knew she didn't have to knock; she could go straight in since she was practically part of the family. Roy's brothers were slurping bowls of porridge and his grandad had his ear right up to the wireless, which was blasting out a play in clipped English in contrast to the homely Glasgow accents as the family spoke across each other.

Roy's mum smiled in greeting as she helped her two smallest children into their clothes and shouted, 'He's out the back, having a sly smoke and getting away from this pandemonium. Christine, will you stop your whingeing and get this here cardie on!'

Doris slipped out of the warm, noisy room and went down the back of the close. Roy was standing on the top step, his head haloed in blue smoke. He didn't turn until she touched his arm.

'Dor, you gave me a right start.'

'You seemed deep in thought.'

'Aye, I was thinking about Hugh. He's been under the weather and I've been a wee bitty concerned.' Roy flicked the ash from his cigarette and it glowed briefly until the rain blackened it.

'Is it serious?' Doris had always liked Hugh, although she was wary of his uncertain temper – which was why she watched Roy from a distance when he went to the warehouse. Hugh was very strict about hours of work.

'Naw, he's probably just getting old. Anyway, what can I do you for?'

'Nothing really. I was getting nervous at home so I came looking for you.'

'Your mum putting you down again?' Roy's eyes narrowed.

'Och, she doesn't mean anything by it, you know that. She puts herself in the situation and how she would feel and then thinks that's how I am too,' Doris said wisely.

'Remember you can do this.' Roy ruffled her hair and she felt the excitement of the touch of his fingertips brushing her temple combined with the frustration of being treated as his little sister.

She pulled away, annoyed with him and herself. 'Aye, I know that.'

For a moment he looked taken aback. Doris was rarely angry and never with Roy.

'Will the rain put people off?' she said, avoiding his gaze.

He dropped the cigarette butt and ground it under his boot. 'Not the folk that matter. I'd guess most of Kiltie Street will come for a nosy. Everyone likes a bargain. Ma's giving up some baby clothes we don't need any more.'

'Annie might buy those. I'm focussing on the wool. As soon as Miss Mearns brings that in, I've to buy it. Me, Elsie and Annie have all chipped in.'

Roy laughed and Doris grinned. She couldn't stay mad at him for long.

'You've got it all planned, Miss Connelly. I'm looking forward to it. Violet's a keen shopper so we'll be there.'

'Violet?'

'My new girlfriend. Didn't I introduce her to you? Never mind, you'll meet her later this afternoon. See you then, Dor. Must go and spruce ma self up.'

–

Doris was still thinking about Violet as she set up the trestle tables along with Elsie and Annie early in the afternoon. The rain had settled to a light drizzle and she didn't even feel it frizzing up her hair or misting her spectacles, she was so… Och! She didn't know what she was or how she felt. Roy and Violet. It had been ages since Roy had had a girlfriend. Or at least one he told her about. She knew he went out with girls but they never seemed to last.

'Doris!' Elsie cried.

'Sorry, what did you say?'

'Your head's in the clouds. I've called you twice. What's the matter?'

'Nothing at all. Here, this table's shoogly; we need something to put under it.'

Elsie laughed. 'That's what I've been trying to tell you. It's like you're away somewhere else. Come on, Doris. We need you. Ah, here's the very man.'

Roy was whistling, hands in pockets, as he approached them. 'Trouble, ladies?'

Trouble. She'd give him trouble. Doris squeezed her hands into fists behind her back. Roy threw her a puzzled glance and all at once she let her arms swing free and her body relax. It wasn't Roy's fault. It was her own for loving him when he didn't love her. That wasn't right, she thought, hunkering down to help push a wedge of wood under the table foot. He loved her like family. But she wanted him to love her as a woman. What did this Violet have that she didn't?

'I hope we get a good turnout,' Elsie was saying chattily. 'Doris advertised it in the post office which was a great idea.'

'I'll go and help Annie,' Doris said. 'We've had stuff handed in already and I see a few folk arriving with bags.'

She felt Roy's stare itch between her shoulder blades but didn't look back. Annie was flustered, trying to take in bric-a-brac and keep Davey from wriggling inside her shawl. Unlike Doris's own limp locks, Annie's hair seemed to take on a beautiful shine in the damp weather, gleaming like liquorice. Maybe Violet had hair like that. She stopped thinking about that as she put out the odd assortment of items on display and stuck price labels onto them – the tags a gift from the woman who worked in the post office.

It began to get busier as people came out of their flats and into the street. Doris and Annie had put up posters in the neighbouring streets as well and soon there was a flow of women gathering at the tables, picking up items and discussing them. A taggle of children roamed the edges, playing marbles and hitting conkers. Doris saw Mr O'Leary putting the world to rights with a couple of other elderly men. It was an excuse to get together and she was suddenly glad they had organised it. *She* had organised it. Although Elsie and Annie had helped plenty, too.

She stood behind the middle table and took in china plates, a toast rack, an old lampshade and a single rubber boot – the other one having gone to the rubber appeal, the owner told her. She laid them out, all the while keeping an eye out for Ada Mearns. She was rewarded when some minutes later she saw the thin, upright figure make her way towards her. Miss Mearns' brown bun was pulled back severely and she was unsmiling. She handed a large bag to Doris.

'There are balls of wool in here. Very good quality but we have no need of them. I want the bag back.'

'Thank you, what a lovely contribution to the Bring and Buy!' Doris smiled and managed to look surprised at seeing the wool. 'I'll pop these in my bag for display and to put a price on them and here's yours back.'

Ada Mearns took her bag without a further word and Doris watched as she went slowly along the trestle tables, stopping when she saw the display of pretty china plates that Annie had cleverly put out a distance away. Quickly, Doris put the bag of wool under the table and paid the money into the tin box they'd brought.

'I can't believe it,' Elsie hissed, arriving beside her. 'My Uncle Leo and his wife are here. They never visit on a Saturday. What am I going to do?'

'Keep calm,' Doris said. 'They're out here, aren't they? The coast is still clear for you to search the flat. As long as they remain outside, you're safe.'

'I see Aunt Ada choosing plates. Did you get it?'

'All safe and sound under the table at my feet. Oh, I can't wait to knit with it. Davey will have a jumper and hat for each day of the year.'

Elsie laughed and then looked at Doris seriously. 'Do you think Annie is all right? I never heard such a terrible thing; that Mr Bale bothering her for his own pleasure. It makes me want to... Och, I don't know what I'd like to do back to him. Something violent.'

'I don't imagine our friendly policeman, Fred Cooper, would let you do that but I've got an idea...'

Doris whispered into Elsie's ear and was pleased to see her slow smile appear.

'Roy's right; you really are a very clever young woman,' Elsie said.

'Was he telling you that?' Doris tried not to feel smug.

'Aye, he was. Told me you read the news to him and his grandad and that you know all what's going on over in Europe. I wish I had a handle on it but I can't afford to buy the papers every day and I won't sit in that parlour with Grandmother longer than I have to so I never hear the wireless unless it's at the factory. *Workers' Playtime* does lovely tunes but doesn't tell me much about our lads and the war.'

'If you want, I can tell you. I read the papers to Roy but I've got it all in my head after.'

'That'd be nice, thanks, Doris. Here's your Roy coming now with a lassie. I'll away and sneak up to the flat.'

Elsie was right. Roy was weaving his way through the small crowd towards her. Doris saw her mum carrying a pot and chatting to Annie's mother. Mrs Morris had an enormous handbag over one shoulder with a plant sticking out of it and Davey in her arms. Roy swerved to avoid the plant and Doris saw a slim, fair-haired girl beside him dressed in ATS uniform. She was ready to run but it was too late.

'Hello, Dor. It's busy, all right. You'll be raking it in. This is Violet.'

'What a lovely jumble sale. I've seen ever so many nice things I'd like to buy,' Violet said cheerfully. 'Roy said it's all down to you. What a super idea.'

She spoke as if she had one of the wee boys' marbles in her mouth but it was hard to hate her when she was so friendly.

'It's a Bring and Buy sale. We're making money for forces' comforts.' Doris couldn't put any bite into her reply. Violet was too nice. 'Where are you from?'

'Helensburgh originally but I'm based in Glasgow now. I like it and now that I've met Roy, I like it even more.'

Doris smiled with an effort. 'Well, it's nice to meet you, Violet, but I must get on.'

She watched the couple walk on to the next table where Annie was intervening between two older women arguing over a ceramic bowl. It wasn't as if Roy was hers. She certainly wasn't as pretty as Violet, not by a long chalk.

–

Fred was tired. He had put in two twelve-hour shifts and his body clock was all over the place. There had been an attempted break-in at a warehouse last night and reports of two men loitering at another location the week before. By the time he'd arrived on the scene, the men had scarpered. The night watchman hadn't been able to describe them; all he'd seen were two shadowy figures running off.

By rights, he should be asleep in his bed but he'd promised to come to the Bring and Buy and had offered a contribution. Besides, it didn't do any harm for the local policeman to mingle with the community. He was there to keep them safe. He looked at the stone bookends his mum had given him. She was working and was disappointed she couldn't come too. The bookends were no use now that she'd burnt the books for fuel. Or rather, she'd given them to poor families whose coal rations had run out.

'Fred, look at this.' Annie arrived next to him, her face prettily flushed. She was pushing a boxy perambulator and looked thrilled in spite of the light rain showers.

'Did you get that at the sale?'

'No, my friend Jeannie's lent it to me – or rather her mum, Mrs Woodley, has. Jeannie's wee brother is nearly two and he refuses to go in it. She says I can have it for Davey until he outgrows it too. Isn't it marvellous?'

*She* was marvellous, a sight for tired eyes, he thought. Her black hair was shining and her brown eyes happier than he'd seen them before. He wanted to reach out and touch her soft skin where her cheekbones were tinted a delicate pink. Instead, he lifted the bookends. 'Where do you want these?'

'Put them in the pram and I'll wheel them over to the table before I pop Davey in it. If I can find my mother, that is. She's greedy over him. Still, it gives me a bit of peace so I'm not complaining.'

He was going to offer to accompany her when he saw someone that made him mumble his excuses to Annie and skirt around to the far side of the sale. It was difficult to hide when he was six foot tall and wearing a policeman's uniform but he had to try. From the relative safety of the end table, pretending to scrutinise a badly whittled elephant, he stared across at his ex-fiancée.

He knew Alice had married someone else since she broke off their engagement. It had hurt when his mother had told him what she'd heard. Looking at Alice now, he thought she'd done well for herself. She was dressed in an expensive lime-green costume with a matching hat and a green feather plume bobbing from it. The man holding her arm was much older than Fred or Alice. He had a balding head but made up for it with a thick, black moustache. What hurt most of all was Alice's adoring gaze as she looked up at her husband. She had looked at Fred that way once until she realised that a riveter's pay was never going to give her 'a comfortable life' as she had put it when she gave him back his ring.

He saw Annie beyond, pushing the ridiculous perambulator and wondered if he liked her because he couldn't have her. There was no risk to his heart from admiring Annie, since she was safely married to another man. Alice had scared him off relationships with women. He doubted he could trust one ever again.

Someone clutched his arm and he smelled a delicate fragrance of flowers. He turned to see Elsie and, for an embarrassing moment, it felt as if all he could see were her eyes which seemed enormous deep wells of blue, like a summer sky.

'I'm going now. Wish me luck.'

'Going?' His head was muddled from lack of sleep and full of Alice and what exactly the shade of Elsie's eyes reminded him of.

'Yes, remember, Ma's papers? I've got to go now while Aunt Ada is down here. So is Uncle Leo. Only, look – my hands are trembling. Wish me luck,' Elsie whispered to him.

He saw her pointing to the man with Alice and realised his ex-fiancée's connection to the Mearns and to Elsie. Before he could gather his thoughts, Elsie had darted away. She swerved neatly round the back of the tables and, without anyone except him noticing, ran up the steps and into the close at number one.

# Chapter Eleven

Was she really going to do this? Elsie's heart hammered as she climbed the stone stairs to the top floor. She was nervous but had a sense of anticipation too. Finally, she was going to get an answer after all the lies and deception. She went inside quietly, hoping to tiptoe across the carpeted hall and into Isobel's bedroom without being seen. But as she took her first step, the parlour door opened. Elsie held her breath. Sarah came out, closing the door behind her and Elsie let out a sigh of relief.

'Thank goodness it's you. I thought you were Grand-mother.'

'You have every right to be here but you've got a guilty expression. Try to remain calm,' Sarah whispered. 'If Mother does come out, you say that you left your hat here and need it for attending the sale as the rain's coming down. As far as she knows, everyone is out. Ada left a while ago and Leo and Alice are visiting but wanted to see the sale first. You haven't got much time; you'll have to hurry.'

'And Grandmother?' Elsie asked, dreading being caught out.

Sarah smiled mischievously. 'We're playing Gin Rummy for matchsticks. Mother can't abide gambling as it's a sin but, strangely, matchsticks don't count. I'm winning but I'm letting her win enough that she wants to keep on going. She won't want to leave the parlour until she's victorious.'

'Thank you, Aunt Sarah. I don't know what I'd do without you,' Elsie said, and meant it wholeheartedly.

'You and Jessie mean a lot to me too,' Sarah said, her eyes moist. She frowned as a clattering noise came from behind the closed door of the parlour. 'I'd better go, Mother has dropped something. Hurry, Elsie. Find what you need and get out before Leo and Ada return.'

Sarah slipped back into the parlour and Elsie heard her asking what had happened and her grandmother's querulous voice replying, although she couldn't make out the words. It didn't matter. What did matter was that she was wasting precious minutes standing frozen on the spot in the hall.

Her fingers pressed against Isobel's bedroom door handle. She couldn't quite believe she was going to do this and for a moment she hesitated. Then an image of Ma and Jessie came to her and her jaw tightened. Elsie turned the handle and went inside.

She'd never been in this room before. It was out of bounds to her and Jessie. She'd never seen Aunt Ada go in, either. Only Aunt Sarah went in with Grandmother, helping her into bed, bringing her treats to tempt her appetite and taking away trays, dishes and laundry as needed. She glanced around. It was fussily decorated and clearly no expense had been spared. The bed was solid oak piled with a dark maroon quilt, a soft blanket was folded at the bottom of the bed and there were several pillows. The curtains were maroon velvet, dark and thick enough without the blackout frame inside.

There was a bedside cabinet, its surface covered in medicine bottles and a silver spoon lying beside them. There was also a dressing table and chair and an enormous dark wood wardrobe. Two shelves running along the wall were crammed with ornaments and an ormolu clock which ticked ominously, as if letting her know she was on borrowed time.

'Where will it be? Where should I start?' Elsie muttered to herself, trying not to panic.

She knew what Ma's box looked like. It was actually a shortbread tin with the delicious biscuits long gone. Ma had liked the tin so much she had kept it for knick-knacks. When the war came along, it had made a perfect place to keep their important papers, as she'd told Elsie. Although she hadn't said exactly what those papers were. The tin was red and green with a picture of a castle on the lid. The colours were faded and some of the colour had flaked off where the tin was dented from once being dropped. It should be easy to spot, so where was it?

She got down on her knees and peered under the bed but apart from a china jerry, there was nothing. She pulled open the bedside cabinet, feeling like a thief. Inside, were more bottles of varying remedies for aching joints and upset stomachs and tonics to give energy. A bottle of Eno Fruit Salts, Cephos powder, Alasil tablets and the blue glass of Milk of Magnesia jostled for space alongside a jar of Pond's Cold Cream. There were cloths and a spare nightgown and a well-thumbed novel by Thomas Hardy along with a black leather-bound bible.

She dashed to the dressing table. There was a beautiful silver-backed brush and hand mirror placed neatly on a crocheted doily. A crystal perfume bottle stood on the right hand side on another doily. There were two slim drawers underneath and she pulled those open to find hairpins, hairnets, a thimble, a fan and a pair of lambskin gloves. A waft of the perfume enveloped her. She shouldn't be here. It was all wrong. This was Isobel Mearns' territory and she was intruding horribly.

But still she had to go on. Looking about desperately, she realised the wardrobe was the only place left. She opened the huge doors to reveal a rack of clothes that she'd never seen her grandmother wear. There were evening dresses and day dresses, a fur coat, a mink wrap and, underneath the hanging hems and fringes of the outfits, a neat row of shoes in different colours and styles.

A very brief twinge of sympathy hit her. It was obvious that these were all from earlier days when her grand-mother had been invited out to parties and gatherings and had walked outside in rain and shine with outfits to match the season, the weather and the occasion. How very sad. Now they hung, unused, in the stale air inside the wardrobe.

On the other hand, Elsie thought, with more asperity, Grandmother could give them to the WVS to dispense to women who would be delighted to use them now that material was very scarce and clothes rationing tightly controlled. She pushed the clothes aside and searched to the back of the space but there was nothing. In despair, she stepped back. Maybe she was wrong. Perhaps her grand-mother had stored the box somewhere else. But where?

She wanted to scream in frustration. She was about to admit defeat and leave when she glanced up at the top of the wardrobe where there was a small stack of hatboxes. She grabbed the chair from the dressing table and stood on it. She was tall and if she stood on tiptoe she could almost see to the back where the wardrobe met the wall.

She carefully pushed the hat boxes aside. She saw a glimpse of red. There it was! Ma's precious shortbread tin had been hidden right against the wall on the top of Grandmother's wardrobe behind the hat boxes. Isobel Mearns clearly didn't want her granddaughters finding it.

'Well, Grandmother, that's tough,' Elsie said through gritted teeth as she reached as far as she could to get the tin. 'This belongs to me and Jessie, not to you and I'll be taking this and hiding it in *my* room.'

She put the tin down on the floor and then stepped back onto the chair so that she could put the hat boxes back in position. There. No one would know anything had been disturbed. Unless Grandmother specifically asked Aunt Ada or Aunt Sarah to fetch the tin, she'd never know it was gone.

Feeling pleased, Elsie stooped to get the tin and froze. Aunt Ada's sharp tones were suddenly audible. Her insides curdled. There was nowhere to hide.

'No, I don't want to play Gin Rummy. What has got into you, Sarah? I never play cards with Mother. That's your job.' Aunt Ada sounded exasperated.

Then came Aunt Sarah's softer voice. Elsie tiptoed lightly to the door to listen, the tin hugged to her chest.

'Did you find something pretty at the Bring and Buy? Why don't you show me? We can sit in the kitchen.'

'I found some very serviceable plates but I don't have time to show them to you right now. Leo and Alice will be coming up soon and expecting afternoon tea. Really, Sarah, you are acting quite oddly. I expect it's your age, although heaven knows I am capable of managing all right and I'm a year older than you.'

A creak from the hall made Elsie shrink back. Her whole body was clammy with fear. She could imagine being thrown out of the house by Aunt Ada and Grandmother when they discovered where she was and what she had taken. Aunt Sarah's voice came again, louder.

'Mother wishes to have an apple pie for tea. She said I was to tell you.'

'For goodness' sake, I've already queued for ingredients for the meal tonight,' Aunt Ada snapped. 'She'll have to do without. I've planned a milk pudding for dessert.'

There was a silence in which Elsie's heart thumped so loudly she was sure her aunts could hear it.

'I'll let you tell Mother then,' Aunt Sarah said.

'Oh, very well. I'll go out to the greengrocer's again. He had some apples, although they were quite bruised. I suppose they will make a suitable pie filling.'

A door slammed and Elsie waited. Dear, sweet Aunt Sarah. She'd saved her. She opened the door cautiously and Sarah waved frantically.

'You must go. Leo and Alice will be here shortly and Ada won't be long either.'

'I got it. Look.' Elsie showed her the tin. 'Thank you for sending Aunt Ada on an errand. I'll hide this in my room and then go back to the sale.'

Aunt Sarah looked pleased and worried all at once. Elsie hurried into her room and tucked the shortbread tin under her bed. She'd find a better place for it that evening when it was safe to do so. She made her way out of the tenement and back onto the pavement, where the Bring and Buy sale was winding up. Women were walking away triumphantly with all manner of odds and ends and children dragged their heels, following. The sky had lightened and the rain almost stopped.

Doris waved to her. 'I've totted it up. We made four pounds and three shillings in all. I can't believe it! We can afford a mound of wool now. The boys at the Front will be warm and cosy this autumn and winter once we've knitted for them.'

'That's grand,' Elsie said. 'Well done.'

'It wasn't just me. It was all of us,' Doris said, beaming.

'We'd better get tidied up. I'll need to head in soon. I'm expected to join in for afternoon tea. Grandmother says it's her duty to include us in the family meals. I'd rather go hungry but I do it for Jessie's sake. She's always starving.'

'You go on. Annie and I can manage. Fred and Roy said they'll help.'

Elsie wanted to linger, especially if Fred was staying to tidy up, but she saw Aunt Ada appear in the street and Uncle Leo and Alice were going into the mouth of the close. She sighed. Jessie came over, her book in her hand.

'Do we have to go for tea?' she asked, her mouth downturned.

'Yes, we do. You know fine well we do. Have you been reading all the while? Did you not find some girls to chat to?'

'I like reading. Auntie Alison said I was to keep reading and when I go back I want her to be proud of me.'

Elsie started to say that she wasn't going back to the Cranstons' but swallowed the words. Jessie looked so unhappy. She put her arm round her sister and they walked together to the close.

'It's going to be all right,' she whispered into Jessie's ear. 'I've got news but I'll tell you later in bed. Right now, let's get through afternoon tea and be polite.'

Jessie squirmed round so she could see Elsie's face. 'Tell me now.'

Elsie shook her head. 'Later.'

Jessie's expression was sullen and she shrugged away from Elsie and stared at her book even as they walked up the stairs. Elsie realised with a pang that she hardly ever saw her sister smile or laugh. Never mind; that would change when she heard about their father. Elsie had kept it from her when she thought they'd never be able to find him. But that had all changed. His address just had to be in Ma's box.

–

Leo Mearns was feeling satisfied. He had been very concerned back in August to discover that his mother had taken Louise's children in. He had told her he didn't want them taking advantage of her good nature but in reality he was concerned that she might become fond of them and leave them money in her will or, heaven forbid, a share in the flat and its contents. It was this worry that had him coming for dinner every Sunday. He could monitor the atmosphere and the interactions between his mother and sisters and his nieces. So far, he detected very little affection, which made him happy but he continued to be on his guard. After all, Louise, for all her faults, had been Mother's favourite. He'd never understood it. As the fifth and last child, and the only boy, surely that should have been his role?

For weeks, he had been brooding over how to get rid of Elsie and Jessie. There had been many sleepless nights when he had rolled out of bed and paced the dark room with an overactive mind. He had come up with very little. How odd, that in the end, Alice should provide the perfect answer.

They were seated around the table in the kitchen. It irked him that Elsie and Jessie were invited to eat with them. In his mind, they were on a par with lodgers. They were not family. Louise had chosen to break off all contact with the Mearns so why should her brats be allowed back into the fold?

Ada brought over dishes of potatoes and beetroot. Before each of them was a plate with a fishcake on it. Leo poked disdainfully at it with his fork. It looked more potato than fish. He put his fork down as Isobel said Grace. He took it up again quickly. His appetite was good and Ada's cooking was much better than Alice's. He wondered if he'd made a mistake in marrying a younger woman. Alice seemed to lack skills in all manner of housekeeping tasks. However, she was eager to please him and he had instilled in her that he liked his meals on time as soon as he came back from work. She also knew not to disturb him when he was reading the newspapers afterwards.

'This is very nice, Ada,' he said. 'Perhaps you would be so kind as to give the recipe to Alice.' There was no harm in flattering his elder sister. He knew he was her favourite, even if he wasn't Mother's. He also made a mental note to tell Alice to fill the damn fishcakes with actual fish.

'Of course, Leo. I'll write it out after we've eaten,' Ada said with a small smile to Alice.

'The news in Italy is looking good,' Leo said, 'I'll eat my hat if they don't surrender by the end of the month.' He was desperate to blurt out his own news but really, it was better to warm the room first, so to speak. He only hoped Alice didn't pipe up all by herself. He frowned at her just in case. Alice's eyes widened and she hurriedly put her head down and concentrated on her half-eaten fishcake, pushing it around her plate and pretending to eat it.

'We could do with some good news,' Isobel agreed.

Ada brought out an apple pie and there was a lull in the stilted conversation. Leo was glad to see that the two Weir girls kept quiet during the meal. As did Sarah, who had always been a mousey sort of woman. He couldn't wait any longer.

'Mother, Alice and I have some news of our own.'

They all turned to him and Leo felt his chest swell proudly. 'We are expecting a son next March.'

'We don't know if it's a boy, Leo darling,' Alice said, touching his arm. 'What if it's a girl?'

Leo swatted her hand away as if it was an annoying fly. 'It will be a boy. What do you say, Mother? Isn't it grand news?'

'Congratulations, my dears. You've made me very happy indeed.' Isobel struggled to rise from her chair and Sarah flew to her side to help her.

Leo embraced her and accepted Ada and Sarah's congratulations too. He ignored Elsie and Jessie as it didn't matter what they thought. Now the rest of his cunning plan could be laid out.

'Wouldn't it be marvellous if we had a wee place to stay here once the baby is born?' he said slowly, as if the idea had only just come to him.

'But you've bought a house in Dennistoun,' his mother reminded him. 'I told you it was rather far away but you didn't listen.'

'I also told you that's where Alice is from and her parents still live there,' Leo said, trying to hide his impatience.

'We would love for you to get to know the baby as much as my parents will,' Alice said.

He smiled approvingly at her. It was the right thing to say. His mother was nodding in agreement.

'What about my old room?' he said.

'But Elspeth and Jessie are in there,' Sarah said.

Leo shrugged to show that wasn't his problem. 'My room would make a lovely nursery and I'm sure Alice and I would be comfortable in there for an overnight stay.'

'You're right,' Isobel nodded. 'It makes sense. Besides, Louise's girls are only here on a temporary basis. That gives them six months to find another place to live.'

-

Elsie was trembling as she and Jessie excused themselves from the table and went into their room. Leo's room.

'Are you cold?' Jessie asked, seeing her shiver.

'No, I'm fair raging, that's what I am,' she replied, looking around her. It was a cold, sparse room but it was all that they had. 'Imagine Grandmother saying we're only here temporarily and have six months to find another home and not even telling us to our face but as if we weren't even present! It's too much.' She clenched her fists.

'Well, I don't like living here, anyway. I'll be glad to move out.' Jessie jumped up onto the bed and pulled her knees in under her chin.

'You know what? I'll be glad too. Hang on a moment.' Elsie knelt down and retrieved the biscuit tin from under the bed.

'What's that?'

'The answer to our prayers, I'm hoping. I've got a lot to tell you, Jessie. I've been meaning to tell you for a while but I didn't want to get your hopes up. Our father is alive and in here, we're going to find his address so I can visit him and ask if we can come and live in his home.'

'I don't believe you. Why are you saying that?' Jessie said, bewildered.

'I'm sorry, I've given you a shock coming straight out with it.'

'Our dad is alive? If that's true, why has he never come home to see us?' Jessie's voice rose, her tone becoming plaintive and reedy until Elsie was afraid the Mearns would hear it and come and see what the matter was.

'Hush,' she whispered, until Jessie slumped on the bed. She stroked her sister's hair. 'I'm sorry. I should've told you sooner but I didn't know how to.'

'He's alive. Dad's alive,' Jessie mumbled. Then her eyes shot wide open. 'Why did Ma lie and tell us he was dead?'

Elsie shrugged helplessly. 'I don't know. Maybe something in the tin will give us answers. We need an address for him.'

She sat on the bed beside Jessie and took the lid off the tin.

'Is it there?' Jessie asked, letting her long legs dangle over the side of the bed now and staring into the tin. 'And is my dad really alive? Why hasn't he ever been to see us?'

'Give us a minute.'

There was a small bundle of letters held together with a piece of string. She laid those aside, assuming that they were from their father to Ma. Below them, were their birth certificates and Ma's wedding certificate. A thrill ran through her to see Michael Weir's name on it. Somehow, it made him real. Which was a daft notion. Of course he was real. And if she could find his address and seek him out, she would see him in the flesh. The address on the wedding certificate wasn't likely to be where he was now, though, since it was dated 1919.

'Look at those!' Jessie laughed and reached over her to take out a tiny pair of knitted mittens. 'Were these mine?'

'I think I remember you wearing them when you were a wee baby, yes. Probably I wore them before you. Imagine Ma keeping them for a memory.' She felt tears prickling the backs of her eyelids. *Oh, Ma. I still can't believe you're gone.*

'Is it there?' Jessie asked again.

Underneath the mittens were a few bills. Elsie had no idea why Ma had kept those. Below them, she found a card with a picture of a Clydesdale horse on the front. Opening it, she saw a few scribbled lines. No greeting or farewell, just an address. It had to be his.

'He's in Glasgow,' she breathed. 'If it is his address, that is. He's well off, then. It's in Kelvinside.'

'What will we do now?'

'The first chance I get, I'm going to go over there and knock on his door.' She picked up the bundle of letters and untied the knot in the string.

'Can I come?'

'Let me go first. It'll likely come as a shock to him. Then we can both go and live with him and leave this awful place.' Elsie smoothed out the top letter, holding both top and bottom as the paper curled in her fingers. She read it through slowly and stopped in surprise. They were letters, all right. But not between Ma and their father.

# Chapter Twelve

'Here you are, love. Buy the messages with this,' Paul said, pushing coins into her hand.

'I'll get us a roll of brisket if the butcher has it,' Annie said happily. 'And there's enough left over for veg and to pay the tally man. I'm glad we don't have to rely on Mum any more.'

'We're going to be all right. There's more where that came from and I promise it'll keep on coming in regular.'

She leaned in and kissed him. He pulled her in for a hug and for a brief moment all her cares melted away. When he held her like this, it was like the old Paul was back again and she could pretend that he'd never lost his arm; that it was just the two of them courting and loving. Paul drew away, shifting onto his heels and already frowning at the door as if keen to get going.

'On you go, then,' she said, trying to make out she didn't mind that he was hardly ever at home.

Paul sighed. He put his hand gently on her cheek and stared into her eyes as if he could communicate without speaking. She wished she understood what he was trying to convey.

'I don't want to be away all the while. But if you want that money, then I have to.' He headed out the door before she had a chance to answer.

It isn't *me* wanting the money, she thought angrily. It's both of us. He made it sound as if she was to blame for all the hours he worked. And that wasn't fair. She and Davey were his family. He was working for them all. Besides, she was doing her bit. She touched the perambulator, which took up most of the tiny hall. It was so kind of Mrs Woodley to lend it to her for Davey. Paul didn't understand the scrimping and saving and borrowing she had to do to keep their wee family going. She had tried to describe the Bring and Buy sale to him and how they'd organised it in order to get the wool from Ada Mearns but he'd hardly sat still at the kitchen table long enough to listen and it was clear his mind was elsewhere.

She thought about last night. He'd reached for her in the night, waking her up by stroking her back. Wordlessly she'd turned to him and they had made love, conscious of the sleeping baby in his cot nearby. It had been quick and frantic and before she woke properly, he'd turned away from her. She'd heard his breathing thicken and knew he'd fallen asleep, leaving her staring at the dark ceiling.

The front door swung open, making her start. Paul was there, his face ruddy from the cold air.

'I forgot to say, Archie will be round with a package this afternoon. You've to be here to pick it up. So, get the messages this morning, all right? I need to race.'

She heard his footsteps clatter down the steps to the street while her stomach knotted at his casual words.

–

He had too much on his mind. No wonder he was forgetting stuff. Paul shook his head, trying to clear it. He jammed his good hand into his pocket as he walked down

Kiltie Street towards town. His other hand, the one that didn't exist, was aching today. Sometimes the pain was so intense he had to prevent himself from crying out. It drove him mad but he couldn't tell Annie. She'd think he was insane. She wouldn't be far off the truth. His head was that scrambled these days. It was all the odd hours he kept. Archie had him taking parcels and notes all over Glasgow, day and night.

He was heading into the city centre now to meet with a man and arrange a drop-off of goods one night. The only benefit that came of it all was the flow of money. Archie trusted him more and more with bigger jobs and, with that, came increasing cash.

Like that warehouse mess the other week. If they had pulled that off, perhaps he'd have made enough payment to stop this nonsense. If only the night watchman hadn't heard them and chased them until he and the other man, one of Archie's henchmen, had to scramble down a muddy bank to escape the police. He wasn't daft. He knew it was risky but what else was he to do? He had a wife and baby to care for. He never again wanted to see Annie miserable the way she'd been when he had no job and that mother of hers was telling her what a waste of space he was.

–

Annie tucked a blanket round Davey as he lay in the perambulator. Was it wrong to feel such pride in owning it? Well, borrowing it, to be truthful, but as she bumped its wheels carefully down the steps to the street she felt proud as punch to be seen. Her shopping bag hung from its handle, Paul's money safely in her handbag over her arm. She planned to make a delicious meal that evening for him. That was, if he was home to eat it. If not, she thought, I'll cover it and keep it hot for him. Paul enjoyed his food and, like everyone these days, he was always hungry. A meal might tempt him to stay home a bit longer.

There was a small crowd outside number four Kiltie Street. She saw Mr and Mrs Woodley and Jeannie, dressed in her work dungarees, her hair covered by a white turban. She pushed Davey over to them, partly to show the baby off in the perambulator and partly out of curiosity.

'Oh, Annie, hello,' Jeannie said. 'We're saying goodbye to Kathy. I've been given an hour off from the factory to do so. Mammy's crying and Dennis won't let go of Kathy.'

'Where's she going?' Annie said.

'She's off down South. She's only gone and joined the ATS.'

Jeannie pointed and Annie saw Jeannie's younger sister come down the steps from the tenement. Her red hair was swept back into a victory roll. She wore a neat blue utility dress with a tweed jacket over it. The jacket was slightly too large at the shoulders but she carried it off well, the way she stood so upright. Her grey eyes flashed with excitement and the scattering of freckles on her pink cheeks somehow made her more attractive. Dennis broke free of Mary Woodley's grip and ran to her. She bent down to the toddler now clinging to her leg.

'I thought she worked at Fearnmore?'

'Aye, she did but she's managed to get permission to join up. That's Kathy for you. She doesn't take no for an answer,' Jeannie said, wryly.

'You'll miss her.'

'I'll miss our fights. We squabble like no one's business but we've got each other's back.'

Annie couldn't help feeling envious. Kathy was breaking free of Kiltie Street and her family and her chores and going off into the world. She was going to get all sorts of new experiences while the rest of them were left here. She stared at the perambulator. All her joy in it had vanished. Now it seemed to represent ties and responsibilities that couldn't be broken.

'I'd best away and leave you to it,' she said.

Jeannie nodded. She picked Dennis up and Annie watched as the toddler reached grubby starfish hands to Kathy. Mary Woodley was wiping her eyes and her husband, Harry, had his arm around her. Annie felt like an intruder. She manoeuvred the pram and hurried away as fast as its clumsy wheels allowed. The movement jiggled Davey and he began to wail.

'Hush, hush now,' she soothed but his little face only screwed up into an angry red colour.

'What is it with you?' she groaned. 'There's never any peace.'

Which wasn't a fair statement at all. He'd improved so much since Doris had suggested the gripe water and swaddling. She knew she was simply taking her mood out on him. She wanted to be the one dressed for action, the one travelling away from Glasgow and all her everyday worries.

She pushed the pram into the main street. There were queues at the butcher's and the greengrocer's shops and she knew she'd have to join them if she was to make that meal for Paul. But she had other messages to run as well and they were a priority. She set off up the road to do so.

By dinnertime she was back home. Davey was fed and sleeping and the small piece of brisket was in the oven cooking. The tatties were peeled. She covered them with water in the pan to wait for the evening. A sad-looking cabbage sat on the table and she moved it to beside the range. She was agitated. When was Archie Bale going to arrive? He was taunting her, she knew, by telling Paul that she was to wait in for a package. He knew she'd be dreading him arriving and by not giving a specific time, she might have to wait all afternoon for him. He had power over her and she hated that.

However, she reckoned he'd come at around two p.m. That was when he'd arrived the last couple of visits. Whether he realised it or not, he had routines, so she was forewarned to some extent. Annie wiped her hands on her apron. At least the evening meal was prepared. Now all she had to do was wait. She picked up her polishing rag and went into the bedroom. Dusting would fill the next hour or so.

The knock on the door just after two o'clock made her stomach lurch. She squeezed past the pram and opened it. Archie Bale leered at her.

'There you are, hen. It's a heavy parcel, so mind how ye go.'

She took the brown paper-covered item tied with string, and for a moment thought with relief that he wasn't coming in but he followed her. He had trouble getting past the pram and the hall was too small for her to stand comfortably away from him.

'Put it in that there perambulator,' Archie ordered. 'I see you've been busy spending my hard-earned cash.'

She didn't bother to correct him. She was too conscious of his bulk right next to her in the cramped space. He scratched his ear and stared at her. Annie put the parcel down on Davey's blanket in the pram.

'Paul away, then?'

Annie nodded. She wanted to lie but what was the point? He would find her out easily. Archie licked his lips. His eyes flickered from Annie to the pram to the bedroom door. He moved towards her and she flattened herself against the pram, feeling its handle dig into her back.

'Aw, don't be like that, Annie. You want to be nice to your husband's boss. Say you'll be nice. Go ahead, say it.'

'I'll be nice,' she whispered.

He touched her breast and she tried to wriggle free but he was in her way and he was too large, too heavy to escape from. His other hand was on her waist and it slid lower. At once, she let herself relax, all the resistance gone. He wasn't expecting it and his hands dropped. She slipped sideways and out of his grasp.

'Let's have a drink first,' she said and managed a smile.

'Aye, why don't we? You're a smart girl. There's no point in fighting this. I'll be good to ye.' He winked and she shuddered inwardly.

The kitchen door was shut and she felt his breath on her hair as she turned to open it and his seeking fingers on her rear, pushing her in. His touch made her want to retch. She flung open the door and dashed inside.

'You're keen,' he said, moving as swiftly as he could into the kitchen and stopped.

The kitchen table was set for tea. There was Annie's brown china teapot with its knitted tea cosy. There were four blue teacups and matching plates and a bowl with small rounds of shortbread. Doris sat on one side and Elsie on the other. Annie took a seat between them, her breathing unsteady.

'Good afternoon; you must be Mr Bale,' Doris said politely. 'Annie said you were coming to visit. Will you

173

join us for tea?' She pointed at the empty place at the table.

'We've been dying to meet you,' Elsie said. 'Annie's told us such a lot about you that we really felt we had to introduce ourselves. I'm Elsie and this is Doris. We're Annie's best friends. We would do anything for her.'

'That's right.' Doris nodded with a cheerful smile. 'We all stick together, don't we, girls? And we all live so close we can be at each other's houses very quickly if we need to.'

'Tea, Mr Bale?' Annie said. She forced herself to look him in the eye to make sure he got the message. His muddy brown gaze met hers and she saw defeat there.

'I've got another appointment so I'll say goodbye to youse ladies.' He retreated into the hall and they heard him leave the flat.

'Is he really gone?' Annie whispered.

Doris leapt up and went to check. She came back smiling. 'He's gone and I doubt he'll be back any time soon.'

'Did you see his expression when he saw us sitting here ready for afternoon tea?' Elsie giggled.

'His mouth was so far open I could see his tonsils.' Doris grinned.

'Like he was catching flies,' Annie agreed with a snort of laughter.

It was a blessed release and suddenly she couldn't stop. Doris and Elsie began to laugh too and it was a while before they could stop – thumping the table, tears rolling down their cheeks and faces flushed with jollity. Annie took in a huge breath and hiccupped. That set Doris off again and when Elsie saw her creased up, she giggled while Annie's hiccups only made it all worse.

Finally, a peaceful silence descended.

'Let's eat this shortbread. It's a crime to let good food go to waste,' Annie said, wiping her eyes. 'Eat up, girls and I'll pour the tea even if it's likely cold by now.'

'I'll have to eat quick. I told Franny there was a family emergency and I'd be back as soon as I could,' Doris said. 'Thank goodness he did come at two o'clock like you guessed.'

'You didn't mind me nipping in this morning to tell you?' Annie said.

'Of course not. It's what we agreed, isn't it?'

'It was a clever plan of yours, Doris,' Elsie said. 'I don't believe he'll bother Annie again now that he's seen she's not alone. He knows that we know.'

'Will you get into trouble for leaving work?' Annie asked. 'I didn't know what else to do. I left a message with the man at the factory gate and had to keep my fingers crossed that it got to you.'

'I got it and then I pleaded a headache to my supervisor. I'll go back now and say I feel so much better. I don't feel guilty because you needed us. If we hadn't been here...'

Annie shuddered. 'I don't want to imagine what might have happened.'

'Nothing did,' Doris comforted her. 'It's all over now.'

'Thanks to you two. I'm very grateful.'

'That's what friends are for. You'd do the same for me or Elsie. We have to stick together and help each other.'

Elsie broke her round of shortbread in two, frowning. 'Is that Paul's boss?'

'Yes, that's Archie Bale.'

'Does he live up in a big house on the hill above Kiltie Street?' Elsie said.

'I don't know. Paul doesn't tell me anything. Why, what's the matter?'

'It's just… I've seen him before. I don't want to worry you, Annie, but I think he may be involved in black marketeering.' Elsie told them about Louise and being sent to buy gin at Archie Bale's house with the wooden counter.

What had Paul got mixed up in? Annie fretted as she waved goodbye to Doris and Elsie. She had had a notion that it wasn't all above board but she'd ignored her instincts. She was so desperate for them to be all right and Paul was much happier now he was earning and giving her money for the housekeeping. She was happier, too.

I'll let it go just for now, she thought. I'll ask Paul to find another job if he can but I can't tell him to leave off working for Archie right now. He'll be miserable and I'll have to go begging to Mum for money. Paul and I were fighting before and I hated it. For the sake of my marriage, we have to keep in with the awful Archie Bale just for now.

# Chapter Thirteen

'How do I look?' Elsie asked anxiously.

She was wearing an ivory blouse over her navy-blue utility skirt, and lisle stockings with her only pair of shoes. She slipped on her winter coat and turned to face Annie. She could depend upon Annie giving her an honest answer.

'Hmm. Wait a moment.' Annie disappeared into her bedroom, leaving Elsie brushing her skirt in case of any pieces of lint. She wished her stockings weren't so ugly. There was a woman up the road who knew an American GI and she had gorgeous silk stockings but Elsie could guess the kind of payment she'd made for them and that wasn't something she was willing to do.

'Here, you can borrow this,' Annie said, reappearing with a beige woollen coat. 'Yours is rather threadbare.'

'Thanks, this is lovely.' Elsie took her own coat off and tried on Annie's. It was slightly too large but she was able to tighten the belt and she had to admit it was better than her own. She couldn't afford a new one.

'Mum got it cheap at a market so it's second-hand but it hasn't much wear on it. You look nice.'

Elsie put on her red beret over her fair hair and smiled. 'I'm ready... I think.'

'I wish you luck. Does he know you're coming?'

Elsie shook her head. 'I tried to write a letter to him first but somehow the words wouldn't come so I decided it was best to go in person.'

'It could come as a shock when you turn up on the doorstep,' Annie said doubtfully.

'He knows we exist. He must expect we would find him at some point. Besides, I need to tell him that Ma's passed on. And that we need a place to live. It's got to be all right. There's no alternative.'

'He's your father so it's up to you,' Annie said. 'But prepare yourself because you don't know what reception you'll get.'

'Why do you never see the bright side?' Elsie snapped. Then she sighed. 'Sorry, I shouldn't yell at you. I'm nervous, is all.'

'Apology accepted. You're going to be late so you'd better catch that bus.'

Elsie realised Annie was hurt by her comment but really it was the truth. Her friend was often gloomy. That business with Archie Bale was partly to blame but it was more than that. Anyway, she had to rush now but she made a mental note to keep an eye on Annie and try to help her. Doris would know what to do.

The bus took her along Maryhill Road and then she walked down Oran Street and Sanda Street into wealthy Kelvinside. Here, there were townhouses and villas and more tenements but these were quite different from those at Kiltie Street. They might be made of the same soft sandstone, blackened with industrial soot but they had wide entrance doors, neat hedges to shade the frontages and behind their façades, each home was made up of several rooms over different levels.

The railings were all gone from the outside walls as she walked along, having been taken for the war effort. Every glance inside the bay windows showed chandelier lights, expensive paintings adorning interior walls, bookcases and overstuffed furniture. There was wealth here beyond her imagination.

She found Pladda Street before the road went across the River Kelvin. Beyond the river were the Botanic Gardens with the famous Kibble Palace conservatory, the aviary and hothouses and its very own railway station to bring in the visitors to the lovely park and its attractions. The railway had closed at the start of the war so there were few visitors these days. A landmine, dropped on the opposite bank of the river during the Glasgow blitz, had damaged the Kibble Palace so it was shut as well. The glasshouses, though, were full of tomatoes being grown for the war effort. It was going to take more than the Nazis to keep Glaswegians down.

Elsie had been there as a child with Louise, who loved to watch the well-dressed ladies promenading and enjoyed pointing out the glorious flowers. She had taken Elsie to see the exotic birds in the aviary and she had been utterly absorbed with their bright feathers and strange calls. They were happy memories and she smiled now, remembering.

Turning onto Pladda Street, she smelled the soapy tang of the river. She might be in posh Kelvinside but the river bore more than a trace of Maryhill's chemical works and the paper works and fireclay works at Dawsholm. At times, the water ran red and blue from the dye works at the end of Gairbraid Avenue. She'd seen a fish in the river once, moving sluggishly with a pale, swollen belly and felt sorry for it.

Pladda Lane was tucked off at right angles to Pladda Street and Elsie walked along its cobbled surface, staring at the large townhouses. Her father was so very near. It was an odd thought. Her whole life she had been told he was dead and all that time he'd been here in the same city and only a bus ride away. It gave her a funny feeling, half excitement and half trepidation. Would he know who she was? Would he be happy to see her?

She stopped outside the middle townhouse and tightened the belt on Annie's winter coat, wishing it fitted her better. She pushed back her beret and tidied her hair. It was no use delaying any further. With a deep breath, she reached over and pushed the doorbell.

It took a few minutes before she saw the shadow of a person approaching behind the frosted glass.

'Can I help you?' An older woman, thin and angular, stared at her with a raised brow.

Elsie fought off the urge to shuffle her feet. She had every right to be here, even if the woman looked as if she thought Elsie should be using the back entrance to the grand house. 'Is Mr Weir in, please?'

'Do you have an appointment?'

'No, but I need to speak with him. Please... tell him Elsie is here.'

The woman hesitated as if she was going to refuse but, to Elsie's relief, she nodded and turned back into the house, shutting the door. As if I might steal something, she thought indignantly, rubbing the toe of her shoe with the other to take off the dust from the cobbled lane.

'Hello?'

She looked up to see a tall man with thinning fair hair and solemn blue eyes which widened in disbelief as he looked properly at her.

'I'm Elsie Weir,' she said.

'How did you find me?'

'Your address was on a card in my mother's belongings. She's... she died.'

'Louise is dead?' He rubbed his hand over his mouth and she saw how lined his face was, deep grooves running from his nose to the sides of his lips. 'Come in, come in.'

She stepped inside onto a shining black and white tiled hall with a tall ceiling and one of the chandeliers she had been admiring earlier in other houses. Ahead of her was a sweeping stairway with red carpet and a polished wood handrail curving up. Doorways led away from the hall and Michael ushered her into the nearest room on the left, calling for coffee to the thin woman who hovered by the stairs.

'Mrs Mahoney will bring us some refreshments,' he said, rubbing his hands together as if he was cold, although Elsie found the house warm after the brisk autumn breeze outside in the lane. 'Have a seat.'

She sat where he indicated on a large armchair covered in embroidered green brocade with a white lace anti-macassar and matching sleeves on the chair arms. Her back was barely touching the armchair in case she creased the materials. She folded her hands on her lap, ill at ease. Michael Weir sat opposite, gazing at her. Between them was an enormous marble fireplace with a crackling wood fire. On the mantelpiece on either side of an ormolu clock were photographs. Elsie glanced at them. There was Michael Weir with a blonde woman smiling out of the frame. There were others of them with two children, a boy and a girl – both blonde – and then later shots as the children grew. Finally, there were two framed photographs of a young man in RAF blue and a young woman dressed in the smart uniform of the Wrens.

He followed her gaze. 'My wife Annabelle and our children, Timothy and Penelope.'

His children. And what about Elsie and Jessie? They were his children too. Mrs Mahoney came in, breaking the awkward silence, and bustled about pouring Camp Coffee and putting out plates, along with a small fruit cake and a silver cake slice. She cut a slice of cake and put it in front of Elsie without asking if she wanted any. She gave Michael a larger portion before leaving quietly.

'Mrs Mahoney doesn't think I eat enough, hence the large piece of cake,' Michael said with a chuckle. 'If you want a bigger slice, do help yourself.'

'This is fine,' Elsie said politely. Honestly, if she tried to swallow it, she might just choke, she was so out of kilter. What was she doing here? Had she made a huge mistake in coming?

'I'm so sorry for your loss,' he said, seeming to pick up on her unease. 'I can't believe Louise is dead, she was always so full of life. Can I ask how she died?'

'She had a heart attack.' *Brought on by too much drink.* But she couldn't say that. Wouldn't say it. She wasn't going to besmirch Ma's memory to this man who had abandoned her.

'I am sorry,' he said again.

'Have you never wondered about me and Jessie?' she burst out. 'Ma told us you were dead so we didn't know to look for you until my grandmother told me you were alive. But you... You've always known about us. Don't you care at all?'

'Of course I care. You can't know how delighted I am to see you. You've grown into a lovely young woman, just like your mother. But it was complicated. I wanted to be a part of your life but Louise wouldn't let me.'

'Will you explain it to me?' She didn't want to be angry with Ma, didn't want to have her memories spoiled but she did want the truth and that was something Ma hadn't often provided.

He glanced at the clock over the fireplace and Elsie knew she had just walked into his life and disrupted it but she didn't care. Then he smiled at her and took a sip of his coffee. He didn't tell her he couldn't spare the time and for that she was grateful.

'I told you Louise was full of life but that doesn't do her justice. She was simply the most beautiful girl I'd ever met. I was back in Glasgow, returned from the Great War, and convalescing at my parents' home when I took a walk one summer's day along the White Cart Water in the woodlands and there she was. She'd dropped her bonnet in the river and I waded in and retrieved it. We got talking and that was that. I started to court her with her father's permission and we were married later that year.'

'But she wasn't of your class. How did your parents react?' My grandparents, Elsie thought. My family, who I've never met.

'They weren't pleased,' Michael said. 'But I was adamant. I was in love with Louise and I was young and hot-headed and wouldn't listen to them. They didn't want to argue as I was still fragile from the war and they were so very grateful that I had come home when millions hadn't. So, they graciously arranged our wedding and paid for it.'

'But it went wrong.'

Michael nodded. 'We were happy for a while. I was training as an accountant and you came along and we were a family. Louise tried her best but she found it difficult looking after you… and she liked a drink. The drinking got worse and then there were the lies about how much she had drunk. She lied about everything, even things that didn't matter. It was as if she made up her own version of the world.'

She knew he was telling the truth. Ma had been like that. Her version was always colourful and interesting but teasing out fact from fiction had been impossible.

'In the end, I left. It broke my heart to leave you and I begged Louise to let me take you out at weekends when I wasn't working but she refused. She said it was either both of you or neither of you. And I couldn't bear to live with her any more.'

'So you gave me up,' Elsie said, bitterly.

'I didn't want to, my dear. Your mother made it impossible for me to see you.'

'She shunned her whole family. She told her mother what had happened and there was an argument and she refused to see her or her sisters and brother ever again. I think my grandmother must have told her to mend her marriage and take you back.'

'How very sad,' he said softly. 'She ended up with no one.'

'She had me and Jessie. You married again?'

'Your mother and I divorced on the grounds of my desertion. I let her have that satisfaction at least, in that I was named as the guilty party. It was a long, drawn-out business with a lot of effort and expense involved and I was lucky that my parents supported me financially and legally. I met Annabelle around that time.'

Elsie looked at the blonde woman in the photograph frames. She had the fine skin and neat hair of someone who had money and she thought that Michael's parents must have been pleased with his new choice of wife. A woman of the same class and upbringing.

'Annabelle was a widow with two small children when I met her. Timothy and Penelope aren't mine by blood but I brought them up and I love them as if they were my own,' Michael said.

'I don't understand...' Elsie murmured.

'Pardon, my dear?'

'Jessie. That's what I don't understand. She's only thirteen,' Elsie said bluntly.

Michael's face flushed a dull red. 'Louise only visited here once. She picked a weekend when Annabelle and the children were away visiting her parents in Edinburgh. I don't know how Louise knew that I was here alone; perhaps she had watched the house. I let her in, hoping she had brought you and that she had relented and was going to let me get to know you. But she was alone and I could tell she had been drinking. Enough that she was in a happy, relaxed mood but she wasn't drunk. We had coffee and talked. Annabelle and I were going through a rough patch and... I'm afraid one thing led to another. It was only one night. I told Louise that I wasn't going to leave Annabelle. I never saw her again. She wrote and told me about Jessie. I sent money for you both, every month.'

Elsie had often wondered how Ma had been able to afford to drink as well as pay rent and put food on the table. Michael Weir's money had paid for it. But looking at the wealth around her made her bitter. He could have afforded more. And if Ma hadn't spent most of it on gin, their lives could have been a lot more comfortable.

'Does Annabelle know about me and Jessie?' she asked.

'She knows I had a child with Louise. I never told her about Jessie. How could I?' He sighed.

'We need a place to live,' Elsie said. 'We're staying with my grandmother at the moment but we've been told we have to move out in six months as our room is needed for someone else.'

'You want to come here? That's why you found me today?'

She nodded. 'I don't know where else to go. You're our father so… you owe us that, at least. We don't need much, just a room. I'm working in a munitions factory and Jessie will be leaving school next year and can find a job.'

Michael leapt up and paced in front of the fireplace, his thumb stroking his chin and his gaze on the carpet. Elsie waited. She found herself looking for a resemblance between them but she and Jessie were the spitting image of Ma; there was nothing of her father's features in them. They had inherited his height, though. They were tall for Glasgow women and much taller than Louise had been.

While her father stood lost in thought, Elsie took in more of her surroundings. The ceiling was impressively high and the chandelier hook was in the centre of an attractive plaster rose. Elegant cornicing trimmed the angles where the walls met the ceiling. The room smelt pleasantly of woodsmoke, lemon and beeswax. In the far corner there was a bookcase crammed with books and the wireless next to it was in a sturdy, ornate walnut cabinet. The house reminded her of somewhere and it took a minute for her to realise it was the Cranstons' home, where she had collected Jessie all those months ago.

She had felt such a turmoil of emotions staying at the Cranstons, ranging from love for Jessie to guilt for taking her away from a place her sister regarded as home. Now she was struggling with similar emotions; love for a father she'd never known, guilt for disrupting his life but also anger at both her parents for their deception and an overwhelming sense of loss that they had missed out on a family life together somewhere warm and comfortable where there was no fear of being penniless or being thrown out by the landlord.

Could she and Jessie be happy here? There was no real choice. Isobel Mearns was going to throw them out early next year and there was nowhere else to go. Elsie felt that Jessie would settle in this house better than she would. Jessie was used to Alison and Donald Cranston's lovely home. Elsie didn't feel at ease here. Not yet. Besides, Michael was so quiet. Was he going to refuse them? She felt a sudden shaft of fear.

'Mr Weir?' she asked.

'I want you to call me Dad,' he said. 'That's what Timothy and Penelope call me.'

'Dad, what have you decided?' How odd and yet lovely to be able to call him that.

'I would like you both to come and live here. You're my flesh and blood and I won't see you out on the street.' He clapped his hands as if his decision was smartly made and then sat on the edge of his armchair, looking at her intently.

'And Annabelle? Will she mind?'

He sagged a little into the chair and then sat up straight. 'My wife is over in Edinburgh visiting her parents and won't be back for a few days. I'll speak to her when she comes home.'

'Will you tell her about Jessie?'

'I'll have to if you are both to come and live here. You leave it with me and I'll let you know.'

'We don't have a telephone and you can't write me a letter,' Elsie said quickly. She didn't want her grandmother or Aunt Ada intercepting a letter. 'I'll come back a week today and we can sort the arrangements then. Thank you… Dad.'

They stood up and he embraced her awkwardly. 'I am glad to have met you, Elsie. You've grown into a very fine young lady. Mrs Mahoney will see you out and I look forward to your return next week.'

He rang a discreet bell on a pull by the fireplace and the housekeeper arrived. Michael watched her go. Mrs Mahoney let her out of the front door, clearly thinking that it was too good for the likes of her but too well trained to say so.

–

'I can't wait to tell Jessie,' Elsie said happily when she went to return the winter coat to Annie.

She was surprised to find Fred Cooper at Annie's flat, sitting at her kitchen table. Annie asked her to join them. Davey was lying in his pram in the hall, shaking a rattle.

'So you're really going to live there?' Annie said, folding her arms and raising her dark eyebrows so like her mother's.

'That's what he said,' Elsie replied, slightly irritated with her friend.

'That's great news.' Fred grinned and she smiled back. 'You found the papers, then?'

'Thanks for the suggestion. Grandmother obviously didn't want me to have them; they were tucked away out of sight and almost out of reach. I found my father's address on an old card and I also found some letters.'

'Love letters between your parents?' Annie asked.

'No. That's what I thought they might be but... in fact, Annie, I need to go. I have to ask Aunt Sarah something. Thanks for the loan of your coat. Bye, Fred.'

He waved cheerfully as the two young women walked out into the hall. Davey gave them a gummy smile and cooed.

'He's a grand wee man, so he is,' Elsie smiled back at the baby.

'Aye, he has his moments,' Annie said.

'Why is Fred Cooper visiting you?' Elsie whispered. 'I was surprised to see him there, especially in his uniform.'

Annie blushed. 'Och, he's on his rounds but he often nips in just to check on me. I've told him he doesn't need to but he says it's no bother. It's because of Paul, see. You remember I had that split lip? It was an accident, nothing more, but Fred has it in his head that Paul meant to hit me. He's just doing his job, that's all. Keeping an eye on the neighbourhood.'

Elsie thought it was more than that but didn't dare say so. Besides, Annie was married so there was no future in Fred being keen on her. There was an unpleasant burn right in her chest when she thought of Fred liking Annie. She fancied Fred. There it was. She had admitted it. She found him attractive and if he asked her out she'd say yes without hesitation. Except he wouldn't. He was too busy sitting in Annie Thom's kitchen.

'I've got to go,' she said.

–

Aunt Sarah was coming out of the parlour as Elsie arrived home.

'Aren't you at work today?' she said, startled.

'No, I've got today off. I was out on some errands. Can I ask you something?'

'Yes, of course. Let me just put these tablecloths in the washing basket for Ada to deal with. Mother likes to have a fresh set every day on the occasional tables in the parlour. It adds to the washing but I don't like to upset her. Let's go into your room to talk. That way we'll have peace.'

'Grandmother?'

'She's reading. I'll have to read out loud to her soon but we have a few minutes before she calls me. Ada is out buying food.'

Sarah hurried into the kitchen to leave the washing and then they sat on Elsie's bed in the neat bedroom. It was easy to keep it tidy because they owned so little. She was still proud of her cheerful rag rug and the second-hand furniture that Doris and Roy had given them.

'What did you want to ask?' Sarah settled onto the coverlet and turned to Elsie.

'Who is Norah?' Elsie said.

# Chapter Fourteen

'Goodness, where did you hear about her?' Sarah said, her fingers flying to her throat.

'Tell me, please,' Elsie said, determined to have an answer. There had been enough secrets already.

'She's your aunt. Norah was my younger sister, between me and Louise in age.'

'Was? Is she dead?'

Sarah sighed. 'She might as well be. Mother cut her out of the family and told us she was dead to her. But as far as I know, she's alive and well and living in Manchester. I do write occasionally but rarely get an answer. How did you find out about her?'

'There were letters in Ma's tin. It looks as if they were keeping in touch on a regular basis.'

'I'm glad about that.' Sarah nodded, her fingers now stilled on her lap. 'I really am. Norah was the black sheep, you see. She was always different. While the rest of us have brown or fair hair, Norah's was as pale as silver. It was quite extraordinary, matched with her almost black eyes. She was spirited like Louise but clever and inquisitive and unconventional.'

'She sounds interesting,' Elsie said, willing Sarah to say more.

'She was – or rather, is. I shouldn't speak of her in the past tense. It's just... hard when so many years have passed without seeing her. She ran away. I was twenty-three so she must have just turned twenty. She couldn't bear living at home with all its restrictions and her clashes with Mother. It was unheard of for an unmarried girl to live on their own but one day Norah simply disappeared. We didn't hear from her for months and then a letter arrived to say she was safe and living in Manchester. After that, Mother forbade us to mention her. She was furious with Norah for running off and causing a scandal.'

'Is she married?' Elsie asked, wondering if she and Jessie had any cousins.

'No, she never married. She must be all of forty-five so it's unlikely to happen now. She has a companion who lives with her. Felicity is a school teacher and they take trips together and walking tours so she isn't lonely. It sounds like a pleasant life in many ways.'

'Two scandals in the family,' Elsie mused. 'Louise and Norah both cast out. No wonder Grandmother can be crotchety.'

'I know she can be difficult but you have to remember she has a lot of pain with her arthritis and that makes her grumpy. And she has high standards of loyalty and duty which she imposes on herself and expects others to do likewise.'

'I'm sorry, Aunt Sarah. I know she's your mother and you love her. I didn't mean to be rude. I wish I found her easier to love as she's the only grandmother I have.' That wasn't strictly true and Elsie thought with a tiny spurt of hope that perhaps there was a Grandmother Weir ready to welcome her and Jessie into the family soon.

'I'm sorry too that it's turned out the way it has. Leo had no right to ask for this room back. He and Alice don't need it. Where will you go? I asked Mother but she refuses to discuss the matter.'

'Please don't worry about us,' Elsie touched Sarah's arm. 'I know something will turn up.' She wasn't going to explain about Michael Weir... *Dad*... until she knew for certain what was going to happen. But she couldn't wait to see Grandmother's face when she announced that she and Jessie were leaving to live in Kelvinside.

When Jessie came in, Elsie hurried to tell her about her visit to their father.

'You saw him? You actually saw him?' Jessie kept saying excitedly.

'I did indeed. Oh, Jessie, you'll love the house, it's beautiful. Dad's well off and he can't wait for us to come and stay with him.'

'Did he ask about me?' Jessie's eyes shone with hope.

'Aye, he did,' Elsie said with a forced smile. She wouldn't hurt her wee sister by telling her that Michael Weir had kept her a secret from his wife. 'I'm going back next week to fix up the details and then we can move in. Don't say a word to Aunt Ada or Grandmother just yet.'

–

After the evening meal, and before she hurried out to Doris's home for the knitting club, she began to write a letter. She picked up the pen and put it down several times, unsure how to begin and what exactly to say.

'What are you doing?' Jessie asked, sitting with her own pencil and jotter, supposedly doing her homework for school.

'I don't know. Either I'm being smart or I'm being incredibly foolish.'

'What's that meant to mean? Who are you writing to?' Jessie sidled over to her and read the top of the letter. 'Dear Aunt Norah…' She looked up at Elsie angrily. 'You never tell me anything. You treat me as if I was a baby. I'm fed up with all the secrets. You're as bad as Ma!'

'That's not true,' Elsie cried, the wind taken out of her at the accusation.

Jessie turned her back, her thin shoulders shaking. Elsie put out her hand to cuddle her in but Jessie shrugged her off.

'I'm sorry. You're right. I should have told you but I only found out today and then it was teatime and Aunt Ada was in a bad mood and she kept me busy in the kitchen.'

'That's just excuses. You could have said when I came in the door. It's my life too, don't you forget.'

Elsie stared at her. Jessie had always been young for her age because Ma and Elsie had sheltered her from their hardships and worries. Being evacuated to the Cranstons who had loved her like their own daughter had kept her innocent too, with books and a playroom and friends at the tiny village school. Sure, hadn't she still played with paper dolls when she came home? Mind you, Elsie hadn't seen her play recently. The dolls were stashed under the bed. She looked at her wee sister with fresh eyes. Jessie was growing up and there was a new wariness to her that Elsie suddenly saw.

'I really am sorry,' she said. 'I won't leave you out again, I promise. If you'll sit with me, I'll tell you who Aunt Norah is and why I'm writing to her.'

–

Annie bumped the pram down the stone steps and out onto Kiltie Street. It was an overcast day with looming black clouds and Davey was tucked up under a knitted blanket. She took a moment to admire her handiwork. Elsie's grandmother's wool had been put to good use. The pale lemon colour was perfect for a baby's blanket. She had knitted during the evenings while Paul was out as it passed the time and had finally finished it yesterday evening at the knitting club. Doris had provided Davey's knitted hat in a gorgeous pastel blue while Elsie promised a pair of bootees soon.

'You look very fine and your Nana will be pleased to see you,' she told Davey as she pushed the pram along, feeling the wheels rattle at every bump in the pavement.

Ivy had not been up to visit for a few days and had sent a letter to say she was under the weather. Annie had decided she would visit her mother for several reasons. The main one, of course, was to make sure that Ivy was all right and that she was simply worn out as she'd written and not something worse. The other reasons were less worthy but Annie couldn't help but have them anyway. She wanted Ivy to know she was managing nicely without her. It irked her when Ivy took Davey with a smug smile and soothed him when Annie couldn't, and when Ivy ran a finger along the surfaces in the flat and tutted when a streak of grime showed. She also wanted Ivy to know that she and Paul were doing well, thank you very much, with plenty of cash coming in and the tally man paid in full. Her mother didn't have to know about Archie Bale and Annie's lurking worry that Paul was involved in some shady business dealings.

At least her business with Archie Bale seemed to have come to a halt. He hadn't been back to their flat and no more parcels had arrived either. She was glad of that. Fred Cooper dropped by more frequently and how would she have been able to explain the brown paper packages? She comforted herself by thinking that she'd have that conversation with Paul soon. Whatever he was doing had to stop. There had to be other jobs, safe ones within the law. Only… the money helped and they hadn't argued for days. Then again, Paul was never around to argue with.

'Stop it. You'll drive yourself mad. Think on something else,' she muttered as she headed up the road to catch the bus into the city centre.

She took the train at Queen Street station down to Dumbarton. After the bombing a couple of years before, Ivy and Annie's home had been destroyed and they were left homeless before being billeted on a farm in Cardross, a small village on the coast north-west of Glasgow. After six months there, they had managed to rent a flat in Dumbarton, a coastal town nearer to the city.

She looked out the window at the fields flying by with their cattle and sheep impervious to the destruction caused by war and the occasional ack ack battery built straight out from the bright green grass. As the train went past Clydebank she closed her eyes, trying to keep the memories at bay and failing. All the horror of the bombs and a long two nights in the shelter before finding their little home flattened and nothing left. Which was nothing compared to finding that their neighbours had been killed. One of Annie's best friends, Janet, had died too. They had only celebrated her wedding a few weeks before the blitz. There had been so much suffering. The sight of the damaged buildings and great gaps where people's homes had completely vanished showed that the pain continued. Most of Clydebank's occupants had dispersed to villages and towns across Argyll and beyond and she wondered if they would ever come back. It would never be the same.

Soon the train was coming in to the edge of Dumbarton and she saw the castle and the Nissen huts where the Polish soldiers were stationed. Along the river were the tall Royal Navy vessels and the whole area was out of bounds for civilians. There was bomb damage to some of the houses, as Dumbarton itself hadn't been safe from the 1941 bombings. One house had a great fracture line running from its roof to its base but it looked as if people still lived there. Another was half gone and a long piece of wood barred the door to prevent entry.

They passed a railway wagon with anti-aircraft guns parked in the sidings at Dumbarton Central behind the library. It was towed up and down between Dumbarton and Glasgow when it was needed – Ivy had told her this with pride as if she personally did the towing. The train came to a stop and a kind gentleman in a bowler hat helped her down with the pram. It had started to drizzle but she had forgotten to bring a hat and she hoped it wouldn't make her hair curl. There was no hood on the pram so she adjusted Davey's woolly hat and hoped he wouldn't mind the raindrops splashing onto his face.

'We'll be there soon,' she said to him as she pushed the pram hurriedly out of the station and past the town hall and across the street.

He began to wail as the rain came on and soon it was lashing down, great sheets of it until she was soaked through. The baby was screaming and she looked down and saw he was sodden. The blanket was dark yellow with water and it was streaming off his cheeks and the rolls of fat under his chin. His little hands were purple with cold and she began to run, jolting the pram wheels and almost tripping in her haste to get to Ivy's flat.

Ivy rented a flat above a shop on the main street. Annie turned the corner and saw the row of shops. The flat was above the green–painted grocer's with its gold painted curlicue sign reading: *'Thomson's Finest Green-grocer's.'* Gasping, she went into the close backwards, pulling the pram in after her. They were out of the rain but she was shivering like mad, her fingers numb as they rang the bell for the upstairs flat. Davey had gone awfully quiet. He stared at her with big, round dark eyes.

'For the love of God, what were you thinking?' Ivy Morris said as the door opened. 'Bringing him out in this! Get him in here now and up these stairs into the warmth. Quickly now, as fast as you can.' She grabbed the baby without even looking at Annie.

Ivy went ahead, Davey in her arms, as Annie bumped the pram upstairs, staggering up backwards and shaking with the cold and with her wet clothes slapping against her legs. Ivy was stripping Davey and wrapping him in towels. Thank goodness her mother had a fire burning in the parlour grate. It was only small due to the coal rations but it sent out enough heat to warm the tiny flat. Annie stood for a moment wondering if Ivy would tell her to make herself at home but when that didn't happen and she saw she was making a puddle on the floor she went into the kitchen and stood on the linoleum.

She took off her wet clothes in front of the range, glad of its heat and, standing there in her damp underwear, she hung her coat and dress and stockings on the pulley. Ivy bustled in with Davey cocooned in the towels.

'You can borrow some of my clothes. You'll need to feed him, he's chilled.'

'I'm weaning him on to solids. I've brought crusts.'

'A feed is what he needs with your warm milk to thaw him,' Ivy said firmly.

Annie went upstairs into her mother's bedroom and chose the least offensive dress she could find. It was far too big but she put it on and then buttoned Ivy's beige cardigan over it. Feeling warmer, she went back down to the kitchen.

'Take him then while I get the range stoked and get some heat,' Ivy told her.

She fed him and held his hands to warm them as Ivy poked at the range fire generating loud rattling, clanking sounds that said more than if she had spoken.

'It wasn't raining when we left,' Annie said.

'You must have seen the dark clouds. It was daft coming down with the wee man like that. You're a mother now, Annie, you have to be the grown-up. The world's not about you any more, it's about him.'

'I came to see you and make sure you were all right,' Annie cried, feeling stung by the reproach.

'Och, I'm fine. I wrote you that. I've been a wee bitty tired, that's all. Travelling up and down to Kiltie Street has worn me out.'

'I didn't ask you to.'

'I'm his nana, of course I want to help out with Davey. And I'll be back up in no time, once I've had a rest.'

Annie glanced up from the baby and saw that Ivy had purple patches under her baggy eyes. It struck her suddenly that her mother was getting old. She clutched at Davey who was now asleep and cuddled him to her, kissing his hot forehead and rocking him. Ivy wasn't that old, she argued silently, but a little curl of fear slithered through her.

'Give him here and I'll hold him. You can get the pulley back down and stretch out your clothes or they won't be dry before you leave. Add Davey's blanket and hat. I've put his breeks and jumper by the range so they dry quicker.'

Ivy took the baby while Annie did as she was told. So much for demonstrating how well she was managing without her mum. Instead she looked as if she was the worst mother this side of the Clyde.

'Dare I ask how that husband of yours is doing?' Ivy said with pursed lips.

'Actually, he's doing really well. He's working long hours and we've got a bit of money put by,' Annie said, leaving out the details. Put like that, it was the truth.

Ivy's black brows rose as high as they could. 'Is that so?' she murmured. 'Well, well.'

'What's that meant to mean?'

'It's not just long hours, it's funny hours he's keeping. What kind of work did you say it was?'

'This and that. It's... piecemeal work for a man that he knows.'

'As long as he's keeping his nose clean,' Ivy said bluntly. 'I hope he's remembering he has a family to look after. He and those brothers of his were always keen on flying by the seats of their pants.'

'I need the lavvy.' Annie got up, ignoring Ivy's pointing finger showing her the way. She did sort of need to go but mainly she needed to be away from Ivy's sharp comments, which were too close to the bone.

She knew fine well where the lavvy was. Ivy was proud that the flat had a tiny indoor bathroom. It had a cold water tap too. Downstairs were the kitchen and parlour and upstairs were two small bedrooms and the tiny bathroom. Annie used it and then stood on the landing, remembering how suffocating it had felt when she and Paul had lived here too. It should have been big enough for the three of them but the obvious tension between Ivy and Paul had made it so difficult she'd been glad when Jeannie had told her of the flat in Kiltie Street for rent.

There was Ivy's bedroom where she'd borrowed the clothes but she gently pushed open the door to the other bedroom. It was like a shrine. Nothing had been touched since they moved in eighteen months before. This was Brian's room, set up to welcome him home. It held the very few of his belongings that they had managed to salvage from the ruins of their Clydebank house along with a new bed, a table and chair and a reasonable quality carpet. His fiddle and a football had both emerged unscathed from the masonry and dust and now they lay on the bed just waiting for Brian to pick them up again.

Annie's mouth twisted. When they'd lived here, Ivy wouldn't let her and Paul use the room. They had slept in the parlour on a mattress which was lifted and set against the wall during the day. If they could have moved out earlier they would have done so. But it was impossible to find a flat or a house because everyone else was desperate for lodgings too. When Annie had pleaded with the Public Assistance Officer he had told her she was lucky to have a parlour floor to sleep on as many families had no shelter at all and were still living in the makeshift rest centres months after the bombing.

She went back downstairs. 'How's Brian?'

'I had a letter last week and he's fine. He's missing home. I gave him our new address again.' Ivy rocked Davey as she spoke.

'Honestly, Mum, you write it in every letter you send. I think he'll have got the message by now.'

'I don't want him getting lost. They could release him any time, you know, and I don't want him coming home to an empty house.'

Annie wasn't sure what she felt. She was fond of Brian but in Ivy's eyes he could do no wrong which meant that if anyone was to blame for anything it was Annie. Besides, the days and nights worrying about him and staying up late to make him meals when he had deserted the army and was hiding up in their Clydebank home had taken their toll on her. She had been tired all the time, snappy and short-tempered with her friends and unable to work at full efficiency at the munitions factory. It had almost been a relief when the military police picked him up after the bombing raids.

'Those clothes of yours should be dry by now,' Ivy said. 'You should get going soon if you're to make the evening meal for your husband. The trains are slow enough.'

'Paul.'

'Mmm?'

'My husband's name is Paul,' Annie said loudly. 'Why is that so hard for you to say?'

Ivy looked startled and then even more so when Annie snatched Davey from her arms. She was livid with her mum. Brian was perfect while Paul was the opposite. She never let up. Even Annie coming to visit out of concern was wrong, apparently. Ivy hadn't even welcomed her or said she'd missed her. No, all Annie got was a complaint that she shouldn't have travelled in the rain.

She had Davey dressed in double-quick time.

'Are those completely dry?' Ivy said.

'You said mine were so I guess these must be too,' Annie snapped.

She bundled Davey into his pram and tucked the blanket around him. She pulled his hat down over his tiny ears to keep him snug. Without another word, she got the pram down the awkward flight of steps and out into the chilly wind. The rain had stopped thankfully but the day was dreich and miserable.

'He looks right peaky, love,' Ivy's wavering voice called after her.

But Annie didn't look back. She stormed off down the street towards the station.

–

Doris couldn't wait to discuss the news with Roy. It had been an exciting and eventful few days on the war front. On Wednesday the Italian government had unconditionally surrendered to the Allies. There were rumours that the Allies were gathering a huge army in Britain for an invasion of mainland Europe. There had been a very interesting article in the newspaper entitled 'The Triangle of Fate' which discussed the German positions in Italy and the fact that the Allies hadn't landed there yet and what the Italians were going to do. It had a helpful map of Italy printed beside the article and Doris had spent a happy hour or two reading all about it and thinking how much Roy would enjoy talking about it with her. Now it was Saturday and the newspaper was shrieking: '*Germans take over Rome, British occupy Taranto*', and stated that the Italian government had declared war on Germany according to a report picked up by the paper's listening station at nine o'clock last night. That report was entitled Radio Rumour and was unconfirmed but if it was true it was good news.

Even if it wasn't true, surely the war must soon be won, Doris thought, hurrying next door with an armful of newspaper clippings. She would have taken the complete papers except that her mum had protested and taken most of the sheets to make tapers for the fire. Doris had to promise to bring the rest back with her once Roy had read them.

It was a damp, chilly day and the air was thick with fog. Doris felt her breath rattle in her chest and hoped she wasn't going to have an asthma attack. The fog was forming a pea-souper, full as it was of soot flecks from the coal fires and industries that made Glasgow buildings so blackened.

She was glad to push open the door to the Allens' flat and make her way inside with a shout of hello. She coughed after calling out and her glasses were steamed up but the room was warm because of all the bodies and her lenses cleared quickly. Roy's mum smiled at her as the two boys and Christine wriggled into their coats and jumped about.

'How's yourself?'

'I'm fine, thank you, Mrs Allen. I brought the papers for Roy.'

'Och, hen, he's not here.' Mrs Allen spun round to her youngest with a yell. 'Will you stop that, Christine, this minute. Do you hear? If you've got your coat on, then out you go and run about and don't come back 'til ye've ate yer piece. Boys, go on with youse an' all.'

Doris had a moment to register Roy's absence before she was almost knocked off her feet by his younger brothers and sister racing out onto the street to play.

'You're welcome to stop by,' Mrs Allen said cheerfully. 'You can keep Grandad company. I've just to nip out with a tonic for Mrs Lennox. She's no' keeping too well. It's her kidneys, see. She has to pee every half hour. I'll no' be long.'

Before Doris could ask about Roy, Mrs Allen had whipped on her shawl and vanished from the room. It was quiet all of a sudden and Doris was left standing with her mouth open and Jock Allen grinning at her from his post by the heated range.

'So, Roy's not here?' she said in dismay.

Roy was always here on a Saturday afternoon. He usually slept until midday in spite of his family's noise and then he was up and ready for Doris and a chat. After that, she knew he worked at the yard for hours until it was time for him to go to the warehouses in the evening.

'He's out with that Violet,' Jock Allen informed her.

'Oh.' Doris sagged against the kitchen table. The newspaper clippings slid from her fingers onto its scarred wooden surface.

'Did you want a cup of tea, hen?' Jock asked kindly.

'I don't know.'

'Well, while you're thinking on it, could you fetch me one?' he said hopefully.

Doris poured two mugs in a daze. Roy and Violet. Roy and Violet. Was it serious, then? It must be for him to be away on a Saturday early afternoon. He knew Doris came to visit and brought the papers. Roy loved discussing the news with her. It was their... *ritual*.

'Don't take on so. If I know young Roy, this lassie won't be around too long. He never keeps the same one for more than a week or so.' Jock smacked his lips in appreciation of the caramel-coloured brew.

Doris set her own mug down. It tasted of ditch water.

'It's just… I always bring the news. Roy loves reading about what's going on with the war. And it's exciting this week; there's big things afoot,' she said lamely.

'He's a good lad, our Roy,' Jock said. 'He's got a quick brain for facts and figures but he's none too fast when it comes to women. He's not worked it out yet but he will. You have to be patient.'

Doris felt a chill which had nothing to do with the weather. 'You know.'

Jock nodded. 'It's a bit bleeding obvious, hen, mind my French.'

'Is it obvious to Roy?' Doris cringed.

Jock shook his head. 'Naw, that's what I'm telling you. He'll be over this Violet in no time and then, there's your chance.'

'He never… he doesn't see me that way,' Doris cried.

'Mebbe he will eventually.'

Eventually! Doris doubted it and what did Roy's grandad mean with 'eventually'? She had a vision of her and Roy all grey and stooped with age and him finally kissing her with dry, withered lips. No, it wouldn't do. She had to face facts. Roy didn't fancy her and he never was going to. She had to stop loving him and find someone else. If that was possible. How many men wanted a small, thin girl with asthma and spectacles like bottle glass? And there were no other men that she fancied. Oh, it was a mess!

'I've got to go. I'll leave the papers here for Roy if he wants them.'

Tears were threatening when she got back home. Leila was bundling clothes into bags ready to take to the WVS centre. She didn't look up at Doris, she was so busy trying to stuff too many items into the bags.

'That was quick,' she puffed, standing up, hands on hips, looking at her handiwork.

'Roy was out,'

'Stick the papers in the kitchen or be a good girl and make the taper twists for me.'

'I left the papers over there.'

Leila looked at her then but Doris had dried her eyes by now and was doing her best to hide her distress.

'Why did you do that? Never mind, you can do something else for me. Mr Gibb has cut the lawn in the back court.'

'That's nice,' Doris mumbled.

'That's just the problem. It's not nice at all. He's cut our half and then left all the clippings in a heap. Oh, he's tidied up his half very nicely but everything else has been shoved onto our bit.'

'I can't deal with it right now, Mum. Can I do it later?'

'He's a horrible man. I don't know why he's picking on me, I really don't. But it gives me the shivers thinking about it,' Leila said plaintively.

Doris didn't like Mr Gibb either and the thought of confronting him was too much. She really was her mother's daughter, she thought gloomily. They were both afraid of the world. Roy had told her she had to stick up for herself. That was all very well, but where was Roy now? Out with bloody Violet, that's where. With a groan, Doris ran into her room, flung herself on her bed and cried her eyes out.

# Chapter Fifteen

By the evening the fog had lifted, leaving the sky clear and the air sharp. Annie stood in their bedroom staring at Davey in his drawer. She could hear Paul stumbling about in the kitchen. He'd had a couple of fingers of whiskey after their meal. The bottle of whiskey was no doubt a payment of sorts from Archie Bale. Annie would rather that Paul had been paid with money. She knelt down beside her baby. Davey was asleep but he had been pale and listless all day. Was there a bit more colour in his cheeks now? All the way back in the train yesterday she had fretted about him in between fuming at her mum but he'd seemed all right last night.

She went to the bedroom door. 'Paul?'

He grunted, coming out of the kitchen with a bleary gaze.

'I'm worried about Davey. I don't know if he's well. Will you come and look?'

He followed her with a belch that stank of whiskey. Annie screwed up her eyes and wafted it away. She knew better than to say anything. In this mood, he was likely to bellow at her. Paul staggered over to the drawer and looked down. He was having trouble focussing.

'He's awful pale, isn't he?' Annie said, chewing her lip.

'Looks peaceful enough to me. He's asleep, isn't he?' Paul slurred.

'Aye, he's asleep but...'

'You worry too much, Annie. Worry about the wean, worry about me. Archie says you're a born worrier and he's right. Women's hysterics, says Archie. Not to be trusted. Let him sleep it off. I'm away to the pub.'

'But Paul...' She grabbed his sleeve to stop him but he jerked his arm away and stumbled to their front door. 'Have you not had enough to drink already?' she cried desperately.

He looked at her contemptuously before swinging away and slamming the door behind him. Annie let out one great cry before pressing her lips together firmly. She ran back to the bedroom and sat on the floor beside the drawer. Was Paul right? Was she overreacting? An hysterical woman, he'd called her, quoting Archie Bale's words. Archie was covering himself in case she ever complained of him touching her, she realised. He would deny it all and say she was making it up.

She must have dozed off because when she opened her eyes the room was dark. She touched Davey's head and it felt hot. Panicking, she picked him up and put her cheek to his forehead to check. He was burning up. His head lolled onto hers and he mewled. What was she to do? What was best? She was full of jumbled up thoughts and for a moment she couldn't move at all. She wanted Paul but he wasn't there. He'd be useless anyway, full of drink and befuddled with it. Galvanised by fear, she put on her shawl and tied Davey into it. He wasn't making any sound at all now. She thought of all the times she had been annoyed at his crying and felt a terrible guilt stab right into her bones.

She walked as quickly as possible to the end tenement, trying not to jar Davey. Doris answered the door on her first knock.

'Annie, what is it?'

'It's Davey. He's… he's not well. Paul's out and I've no one else. Will you run for Dr Graham for me?'

'Come away in. What's the matter with him?' Doris waved her in and shut the door on the cold night air.

'He's feverish. It's all my fault. I should never have… Can you get the doctor?' Annie moaned.

'It's no good,' Doris shook her head, looking scared. 'Dr Graham is over at number five. Old Mrs Lennox took a nasty turn. My mum's over there too. It's not looking good. The doctor will be tied up for hours.'

'What am I going to do?'

'Wait here. I'll fetch Elsie. Three heads are better than two.'

Annie rocked Davey and kissed his soft, hot head. She sang lullabies to him and tears streamed down her face unheeded. She hadn't been a good mother to him, Ivy was right. She had been careless, taking him out to get soaked yesterday because of her stupid pride. She'd wanted to show Ivy she was coping. Instead, she had made her baby sick.

'It's all my fault, son. All mine. What will I do if anything happens to you?' she murmured, feeling the heat rise off him onto her mouth as she hovered over him so closely.

'It's going to be all right, Annie,' Elsie said behind her. 'Me and Doris are here for you. If the doctor isn't around, who else can help? Think hard.'

Annie's brain was mush but a single thought rose up. 'The midwife. Mrs Wiley. She'll know what to do.'

'Do you know where she lives? I can go and fetch her,' Elsie said. She had her coat and hat on and was ready to go.

Annie looked at Davey and shook her head. 'No, I'm not waiting. I'll take Davey to her. I know the address.'

'We're coming too,' Doris said.

Annie barely waited for Doris to get her coat on before leading them along Kiltie Street and up the back roads to the old railway cottages. She had visited Mrs Wiley once when she was pregnant, wanting to introduce herself to the woman who would deliver her baby. Even in the blackout she knew the way. Doris held her arm on one side and Elsie kept a hold of her on the other. Between them all was Davey, cocooned in Annie's shawl. She thanked God for her good friends as they hurried up the path to Mrs Wiley's cottage.

She hardly registered Fred Cooper's surprised face as she pushed past him into the warm, brightly lit interior of the railway cottage. She heard Elsie speaking but it was as if her ears were full of bees, buzzing in a multitude.

'Why are you here, Fred?' Elsie was saying.

'I live here. Are you looking for me or my mum?' came Fred's deep voice replying.

'We need Mrs Wiley. Is this the right cottage?' She heard Doris ask.

'This is the right place. Mrs Wiley is my mum,' Fred explained.

None of it mattered. Annie had tunnel vision. All she wanted to see was Mrs Wiley. And suddenly, there she was. Annie's knees went weak at the joints and she stumbled forward.

'Please… please do something. Davey's not well. He's hot and he's not crying any more.' She thrust her baby into

Mrs Wiley's comforting arms and sagged to the floor. She was vaguely aware of someone, maybe Elsie, picking her up and then both Elsie and Doris were supporting her into the Wileys' warm, cosy kitchen. An older man got up from the table and went out.

'That's my Bert,' Monica Wiley said as she carefully checked Davey over. 'Fred, be a good lad and put the kettle on while I see to this wee man. Then you can keep your father company in the parlour. I'll be needing the kitchen.'

Annie felt her legs shake as she sat and watched the midwife strip Davey. Monica's face was serious as she touched him. With his clothes loosened, he was a tiny creature and a great love and tenderness washed over her as she looked at her baby, along with a fierce protectiveness. She would do anything for him. It was a primeval instinct and it struck her with a storm force.

She loved him. She had resented him for so long. She had blamed her baby for the rift between her and Paul. She had almost hated him for his relentless crying and gurning. What was wrong with her? Was she some kind of monster? She took in a raw, hacking breath and the noise of it was loud.

'Don't despair,' Monica told her, briefly putting her hand over Annie's. 'He has a fever but we're going to sponge him with tepid water until it goes down. He's a wee bit dehydrated too so I'll want you to feed him and then we'll top him up with water too. All right?'

Annie nodded. Whatever it took, she would do it. *Oh, Davey!* She would give her life for his. Why had it taken this for her to realise how much she loved him? He wasn't a burden. He was her son.

'We'll be in the parlour if you need us,' Elsie said.

Annie barely noticed them go and Fred with them. She had eyes only for Davey and the midwife tending him.

–

Elsie and Doris sat in the neat parlour with Bert and Fred. There was a small fire burning in the grate which kept the room warm and the wireless was on low with slow jazz playing in the background. Bert had persuaded Doris to play him at Nap and they sat in the armchairs with a small table between them for the cards. That left Elsie sitting with Fred on the sofa. She was acutely aware of the small space between her leg and his and tried to ignore the way her skin tingled at his nearness. Besides, worry for Annie and Davey almost overrode her feelings for Fred right now.

'Doctor Graham is busy and we didn't know where to turn,' she said. 'I hope Davey's all right, I don't know what Annie will do if...'

Fred reached for her hand and squeezed it reassuringly. Elsie tried not to gasp out loud. Could he feel the electricity between them too?

'Mum is every bit as expert as Doctor Graham when it comes to babies, I promise,' he said. 'Davey's in good hands.'

'Oh, I didn't mean... that is... I wasn't trying to say she wasn't,' Elsie spluttered awkwardly.

Fred grinned. 'Don't worry, I know what you were trying to say. I got a shock opening the door to you and Annie and your friend Doris.'

'Not as much as we did.' Elsie laughed, glad to change the subject. 'Annie never said you were her midwife's son.'

Fred laughed too. 'I don't suppose she knew. After all, we have different surnames. My dad died when I was young and Mum married my stepdad, Bert. I call him Dad as he's been as close as my own dad was to me growing up. I couldn't ask for a better father.'

'You've been lucky,' Elsie said wistfully. 'I wish I'd known my dad while I was growing up. Still, I hope I'll get a chance to get to know him better soon.'

'You going back to see him next week?'

Elsie nodded, feeling the excitement rise inside her. 'I can't wait for me and Jessie to move out of Kiltie Street and away from my grandmother. You should see my dad's house, Fred. It's enormous. There's more than enough space for him and my stepmother and their grown-up children and ourselves.'

She realised she was still holding Fred's hand when he gave it another gentle squeeze to show his delight for her. She pulled hers away slowly, not wanting to seem forward. Just as well she had, too, she thought, for here was Fred's mum coming into the parlour. Her gaze flicked between Elsie and Fred, and Elsie wondered if she had seen them holding hands. Not that Fred had put any store by it. He was just being nice.

'How's Davey?' Doris asked, from her position in the armchair, her cards paused on the table.

'We're sponging him and hoping his temperature comes down. He's had some water and Fennings' Cooling Powders to drink and we'll see how we go. I don't think we need the doctor yet and if we're lucky, we won't need him at all. Annie's going to stay the night with us. Fred, be a love and bring the spare bedding down from the cupboard upstairs. There's enough to make a comfortable bed for Annie on the kitchen floor and we'll keep the fire stoked. We can't have Davey getting too cold either.'

Fred got up obediently and kissed his mother on the top of her head as he passed. She pushed him playfully and Elsie could see there was deep affection there. What a nice family, she thought. Bert was laughing and teasing Doris and her small friend's face was flushed with triumph as she slammed down another Nap trick. Elsie felt she could happily stay here forever. How different the atmosphere was from the Mearns' flat.

Monica Wiley sat beside her. 'He's a good lad, my Fred.' She nodded in the direction of the door. 'Nothing's ever too much bother for him and he works very hard as a policeman on the beat round the neighbourhood on top of his job at the shipyard.'

'He helped carry my furniture up to my flat when I moved in,' Elsie said. Saying it was her bed that Fred had carried seemed a bit too intimate, which was silly.

'That sounds like him. Give the coat off his back, he would. He's a catch for any girl but he's had his fingers burnt. Here's me that loves babies and just as well, with my job, but I doubt I'll ever hold a grandchild of my own.'

Elsie was dying to ask how Fred had got his fingers burnt and why he would never produce a grandchild but she needn't have worried because Monica was chatting again in a confiding tone.

'See, he was engaged to this girl, Alice, and he adored her. But didn't she up and jilt him two days before the wedding! Turns out she'd found a wealthier man. In fact, you might know of him. The family lives in Kiltie Street near Annie. A Leo Mearns?'

*That Alice.* Elsie could hardly believe it. Alice Mearns had once been engaged to Fred Cooper. Poor Fred. She felt he'd had a lucky escape, having seen Alice at many Sunday dinners and not warmed to her at all.

'I hope you won't hold it against me, Mrs Wiley, but I know Alice. She's married to my Uncle Leo. They don't like me or my sister at all but I have to say the feeling's mutual. They don't live in Kiltie Street now; they have a home in Dennistoun so Fred won't bump into them.'

'It should all be water under the bridge by now,' Monica confided. 'It's been almost a year but Fred hasn't had a girlfriend since that girl broke his heart and put him off marriage.'

Elsie didn't know what to say. She didn't want Fred to be unhappy but she couldn't help her heart lifting a wee bit when she heard he didn't have a girlfriend. She also had a sneaking suspicion that his mother was doing a bit of matchmaking. If only it would work. But if Fred liked her that way, surely he would have asked her out by now? And what about his feelings for Annie?

When Fred came back, Elsie and Doris got their coats on. Doris had won at cards and Bert invited her back for a re-match. Monica insisted that Fred walk them home as it was dark and he said he had been going to do so anyway, with a wink to Elsie which made her insides churn deliciously. They poked their heads round the kitchen door and whispered goodbye to Annie, careful not to disturb Davey who was asleep. Elsie enjoyed the short walk back to Kiltie Street as they chatted. Doris was thrilled with her win and described the tricks and Elsie was content to listen to her and Fred's deep voice answering. She sent up a prayer for Annie and Davey and decided to pop in the next day once they were home to check on them.

Back in her room, she picked up the letter that had arrived that morning from her Aunt Norah.

*My dear Elsie.*

*I was so terribly sorry to hear of your mother's passing and hope that you and Jessie are bearing up well. Sarah wrote to tell me the sad news but I'm afraid I was so upset that I didn't write back to her. I'm actually a terrible correspondent, my dear, so I am warning you now. You may get six letters in a row from me and then nothing for months!*

*And yes, that means I want to write to you and get letters back and catch up on all the lost years, getting to know you. Dear Louise's daughters! What a find for me. I may have lost my darling sister but God has gifted me you and Jessie.*

*Goodness, we have so much to tell each other! I want to hear all about where you grew up and what life was like with your lovely mother. In return, I shall tell you all about the exhilarating hikes that Felicity and I take whenever we get a chance to get outside the city. You will love Felicity as much as I do when you meet her (and you must come and visit, do promise) as she is full of fun and a great friend and confidante.*

*We are terribly busy with our war work but we have to take Chopin for daily walks. Not the composer, of course, but our dear little border terrier. There's Norman, too. He's the lodger. We don't take him for walks but he is rather musical and after a couple of sherries quite inclined to partake in a jolly singsong as we have an old piano that is mercifully in tune.*

*I must race as I'm writing this early morning before my shift at the factory begins. There's a funny story I will relate in my next letter about the fire-watching that I do in the evenings on the factory roof. Remind me, if I forget.*

*I shall leave you now in the hope of a swift return letter from you, my dear.*

*Your loving Aunt Norah*

Elsie smiled as she re-read it. Her aunt could certainly paint a picture with her words. She found a piece of her own precious writing paper and began to compose a reply. Perhaps she'd tell Aunt Norah about finding her father, about Annie's baby and, of course, some stories about Ma and Jessie and their home life.

–

'You've got good friends, dear,' Monica said, going back through to help Annie sponge Davey with lukewarm water once more. 'Now, how's this wee man doing?'

'I don't know if he's any cooler or not. He sleeps a bit and then he's restless again.'

'Then I'll stay up with him until it resolves. You try and get some rest. Fred's made up that bed and it should be comfortable.'

'No, I can't sleep when Davey's so poorly.' Annie shook her head firmly. 'I'll stay up too; we can take it in turns to wash him.'

Monica nodded. 'If he doesn't turn a corner soon it will be a trip to the hospital, I have to warn you. He may have an infection and I can't treat that here.'

Annie trembled as she wrapped Davey's clothes loosely round him. *Please God, I'll do anything. Only don't take my baby from me.*

Towards dawn, Davey's fever broke and the two women looked at each other with relief. Annie saw her own exhaustion reflected in Monica's dark-circled eyes and pale cheeks.

'Get some sleep,' Monica said gently. 'I'm away up to my bed but I'll see you for breakfast.'

'Thank you with all my heart,' Annie said fervently. She laid Davey onto the bedding and hugged the older woman tightly. The moment was broken by a huge yawn and they both giggled silently.

Annie got into the bed carefully and drew Davey in beside her. She didn't want him to get overheated but she had to have him near. She nuzzled his forehead where his soft hair grew in little tufts and inhaled his damp baby scent. He was so precious. It had taken a terrible scare for her to truly appreciate him. Now, she promised him, he was number one and everyone and everything else came second to caring for him.

–

She got home to Kiltie Street later that morning after having breakfast with Monica, Bert and Fred. Monica was preparing for two babies due to be born that day while Bert was heading for his garage and Fred's shift was starting. He walked part of the way with her and waved as he split off to follow his beat.

'Where the hell have you been?' Paul shouted. 'I've been out of my mind thinking you and the wean had been knocked down in the blackout or worse.'

She smelled the beer on his breath and saw his red-rimmed eyes. His face was crumpled with sleep lines and he had clearly slept in his clothes from the day before. An acrid smell of armpits reached her, making her feel sick.

'I asked Elsie to knock last night and tell you where I was,' she said. 'But I'll bet you didn't hear because you were so drunk.'

He looked abashed but then stuck his chin out belligerently. 'You're a right old nag, Annie, you know that? It's no wonder I escape to the pub when you're harping on at me all the time.'

'That's not fair,' she cried, stung by his comment. 'I'm trying to stop you getting drunk, that's all. You could have a drink or two but you never stop there, do you? You make me sick.'

'Aye, well. It's mutual. You make me sick an' all.'

They stared angrily at each other. Paul was the first to look away. He rubbed his hands over his face and mumbled, 'What's with the wee man anyway?'

'He was poorly with a fever and it wouldn't come down. Mrs Wiley looked after him. She'll come round later to check on him.'

'How did he get that? It's not measles or worse, is it?' There was fear in Paul's voice.

'There's no infection – or none she can find – but we've to keep an eye on him. If he sickens again, it's straight to the hospital. It was my fault.'

'What do you mean?' He stood up straighter and frowned.

'I took him to see Mum and he got soaked in the rain.' She lowered her gaze, hoping he would understand. She was loaded with guilt as it was. She kept replaying images of the drenched pram and Davey with the rainwater running off him in streams. What had she been thinking, taking him out in that?

'It was your fault,' Paul said coldly. 'You're meant to be caring for him. He's my son and you neglected him. You should be ashamed of yourself.' He turned away from her and Annie let him go. There was nothing he could say that she hadn't accused herself of.

She felt hollow as she changed Davey's nappy and fed him. His big, dark eyes locked trustfully on hers from her breast and she stroked his tiny hand. He curled his fingers around hers, the tiny nails scratching and all the love that had been stemmed for months poured out of her.

'I love you, Davey Thom. I love you more than the world. Your daddy is angry with me just now but he'll get over it. As long as you forgive me, son.'

–

Paul didn't forgive her. What was worse, when Ivy came to visit now that she was on the mend, he told her what had happened and she was livid with Annie too and refused to talk to her. She came up every day as she had since Davey was born and she looked after him and prepared an evening meal but apart from singing and cooing and chatting to Davey as she went about her self-imposed tasks, she said nothing to Annie.

'It's brought Paul and Mum together in a way nothing else has,' Annie told Elsie when she came to visit a couple of days later. 'It's ironic. They both hate me and it's bonded them.'

'They don't hate you,' Elsie said. 'They'll come round. Give it time. The most important thing is, how is Davey? I knitted him a jumper.' She handed Annie a blue jumper with a white trim.

'Thanks, that's lovely. He's fine. He's bounced back and you wouldn't know he'd been ill. I wish Paul and

Mum could let go of the whole affair as easily,' she said, unhappily.

'Family is important, isn't it? Fred has a good relationship with his stepdad and obviously adores his mum. I loved my mum and I really hope I can get to know my dad.'

'Sorry, I've been so full of my own problems, I forgot to ask you about your dad. When are you seeing him?'

'Tomorrow afternoon. I'm due time off from the factory and I want to go without Jessie. I mean, it'll be fine but… just in case, it's best I go alone. Then we can move our stuff over that evening.'

Elsie's eyes gleamed and Annie didn't caution her. She had a bad feeling about it but perhaps that was simply the gloomy atmosphere in her own home rubbing off on everything else. She hoped it worked out for Elsie. In the meantime, it looked as if she was not going to be forgiven by her husband and mum for a good while yet.

# Chapter Sixteen

Elsie didn't dress up especially this time. She didn't want to bother Annie to borrow her coat, and besides, if she and Jessie were going to live with their father, he had to understand that they weren't well off. She buttoned up her coat against the sharp breeze as she stood staring at the River Kelvin. There were three ducks bobbing about on its brown glassy surface, their emerald green heads distinct against the autumn browns and golds as they navigated the ripples where the breeze touched the water. Her shoes had sunk in a little to the muddy banks but she didn't care. She was plucking up the courage to walk along to Pladda Lane and ring the front doorbell.

'Come along, Elsie Weir. Got your nerves under control and let's get going,' she said out loud.

The ducks quacked as if sharing a joke and she smiled. What was she waiting for? Dad knew she was coming. In fact, if she didn't shift herself, she'd be late. Feeling more relaxed, she walked swiftly to the lane where Michael Weir's townhouse stood.

Mrs Mahoney answered the door with no particular sign of recognition.

'It's Elsie. To see my father,' she said, with more confidence than she felt.

'Mr and Mrs Weir are waiting for you in the drawing room,' the housekeeper said without a smile. 'Please follow me.'

She led Elsie to the same room she'd been in before. Elsie's heart was thudding in her chest. Mr *and* Mrs Weir. So she was about to meet Annabelle, her father's second wife. Michael rose to greet her as she was ushered in but the blonde woman in the armchair beside the fire remained seated. Elsie was suddenly sorry that she had trodden in the mud by the river. She had wiped her feet on the outdoor mat but worried that there was a visible tidemark on the leather.

'Elsie, you look well,' Michael smiled hesitantly. 'Do have a seat.' He looked to Annabelle as he spoke and Elsie realised, with a jolt, that he was nervous.

She sat where indicated on a chair with a cream and rose linen cushion and ladder back while he sat in the armchair opposite his wife's. There was a momentary silence between them in which all she could hear was a log sliding in the fireplace and a distant shout somewhere outside on the road. She wondered if she should take off her coat. Shouldn't Mrs Mahoney have offered to take it?

'Tell her, Michael,' Annabelle said.

She was older than her photograph on the mantelpiece and her eyes were chips of grey as they stared at Elsie. Her mouth was a thin line of scarlet lipstick. In spite of her frown, she was an attractive ash-blonde and well dressed with a string of pearls at her neck against a pale-blue wool dress and silk stockings.

Michael rubbed his upper lip and wouldn't meet Elsie's gaze.

'Tell me what?' she asked uneasily.

'Michael. Either you tell her or I will,' Annabelle snapped, as Michael stood up but said nothing, his hands in his trouser pockets, looking as if he'd rather be anywhere but the spot in front of the fire where he stood.

'I'm so sorry,' he whispered, and Elsie put her hand out as if she could stop what came next because she had already guessed that Annabelle had made the decision for both of them and she and Jessie were not going to like it.

'The thing is... Annabelle... well, both of us actually... think it would be too disruptive for Timothy and Penelope if you came to live here.'

'But they're not here! They're away in the forces and your house is large. We'd keep out of their way,' Elsie said desperately.

Michael shook his head. 'It won't do, I'm afraid, darling.'

'But you promised. You said you wouldn't see us out on the street.'

'I... I should have—'

'Oh, for goodness' sake, Michael, tell the girl,' Annabelle cut in, impatiently. 'If you won't, then let me or we will be here all day.'

'Does she know about Jessie?' Elsie cried, wanting to hurt him.

Michael seemed to crumple and he sat back into the armchair, looking at his wife.

'He has told me about that unfortunate incident and its ramifications, yes,' Annabelle said stiffly.

'*Incident and ramifications?* What kind of language is that to talk about my sister?' Elsie cried. 'She's more than just a problem to be swept under the carpet.'

'She is hardly our problem and nor are you. Your mother made it very clear she wanted nothing to do with my husband a very long time ago. You have no right to appear now when it's convenient and try to take up a place in our home. You are not family, nor will you ever be.'

She turned to her husband with barely concealed distaste. 'Michael, will you please deal with this situation the way we agreed. I should not have to sully myself with this. You have dragged your sordid problem into our home and I find that hard to forgive.'

'Dad?' Elsie whispered, hoping that she was wrong and that this wasn't turning into a nightmare. He had promised her and Jessie that everything was going to be all right but it wasn't.

'My dear, I can't do anything.'

She looked at his bowed head with its thinning hair and felt her anger rise. He was weak. Had he really fought to stay in touch with her and Jessie? Or had he let Ma walk away from him because he was secretly relieved to have her out of his life?

Annabelle stalked from the room, her back ramrod-stiff.

'You're not going to fight for us?' she said sadly.

'Annabelle's wealth bought this house and she has reminded me of that,' Michael said. 'It's our home but I don't have quite the say in it that I thought when I told her about you and Jessie. Perhaps she's right about Timothy and Penelope. We can't shake up their lives. Annabelle worries about her reputation too. We have a position to maintain in society and we can't have rumours floating about.'

'Me and Jessie are hardly rumours. We're real and we're yours whether you like the fact or not,' Elsie retorted. She stood up and tightened her belt, almost glad to have it bite into her waist. At least it was an honest feeling. 'Don't bother to call the housekeeper. I'll let myself out.'

He followed her to the door. She stepped outside into the biting wind that had risen up and felt as bleak as the grey day.

'Look, I'll give you money. Enough for you and Jessie to find a place to rent. At least let me do that,' Michael said. His eyes were watering but she couldn't decide if he was upset or whether it was the wind irritating them.

Elsie shook her head firmly. 'I don't want your money. I wanted your love but it looks like I can't have that so I'll take nothing from you. Goodbye, Mr Weir.'

She didn't look back as she walked out of Pladda Lane, the wind whipping at her hair and chilling her legs. She would never go back there. Ever. It was done. If anyone asked if she had a father, she'd say he was dead. He might as well be for all the love and support he had shown.

She made it to the end of the road before she began to shake. She stumbled down the river bank and sat on a bench, shoulders hunched and her mind numb. The ducks were on stormy waters now as the wind lifted the river's surface along its length. The coldness inside her was more than the autumn day. What was she to tell Jessie? Living in Pladda Lane had been their dream and their only hope since she discovered their father was alive.

She sat there until the cold seeped into her skin and her fingertips ached with it. Then, with a sigh, she began to walk towards Kiltie Street. It started to rain but she didn't try to catch a bus or tram. The pounding of her feet on the pavements was somehow comforting. Even the icy trickle of raindrops soaking from her hat onto her face helped stop her worrying about what they were to do next.

Aunt Sarah opened the door to her.

'My dear, you're soaked. Quickly, into the kitchen and strip off your wet clothes. You'll catch your death.'

Elsie was shivering and was only too glad to be shepherded into the heat of the kitchen. Aunt Ada frowned at the sight of her but turned back to the stew bubbling on the range, stirring it with a large wooden spoon without a word. Sarah fetched dry clothes and Elsie dressed quickly.

'Jessie is reading in your room. I'll bring you in another blanket,' Aunt Sarah said pointedly, with a nod in Ada's direction.

Elsie took the hint. They couldn't talk freely in front of Aunt Ada and Sarah was clearly dying to know what had happened with Michael Weir. She padded in bare feet to her room where Jessie leapt up with a grin.

'I've packed a bag. Aunt Sarah bought me a wee cardboard suitcase. Look at it, isn't it great? I've put in my clothes and all my books.'

Aunt Sarah arrived before Elsie could explain to an excited Jessie just where the afternoon had gone so terribly wrong.

'How did it go?' Sarah set the blanket on the bed and turned with an expectant smile.

Elsie's heart sank. She was going to disappoint two people she loved. She watched their smiles fade at her expression. Deliberately, she got up and padded over to the window, staring out at the familiar tenements with their black bricks and slate roofs.

'What is it, Elsie?' Jessie said, nibbling her fingernails. 'What did our dad say?'

'Let me be for a wee minute,' Elsie said brusquely. She knew that once the words were out, they couldn't be taken back. For a moment longer she wanted to keep her dream

228

alive. She imagined how it might have been, living in the beautiful townhouse at Pladda Lane. With a real father and a family of their own, a new brother and sister and even a new mother. If only Annabelle Weir had been a different sort of person, kinder and more forgiving. How terrible that all their hopes and dreams had hung on her decision.

'Oh dear,' Aunt Sarah said softly.

Jessie stared at her bitten fingernails and then at Elsie defiantly.

'There, I've given you a "wee minute" as you put it. Now tell me what happened. When are we moving?'

Elsie glanced at the small cardboard suitcase on the bed beside Jessie and wanted to cry.

'It wasn't our father's fault, not really. It was his wife. She thinks it might disturb their other children too much if we moved in.'

'Aren't they grown up?' Jessie said. 'Does she mean we have to wait a few months? I don't want to do that. I love Aunt Sarah but I don't like living here. Aunt Ada and Grandmother are mean to me.'

'It's not about waiting a few months. We can't move at all.' There, she had said it.

The words seemed to float in the air between them. Aunt Sarah leaned over and touched Elsie's shoulder in sympathy. Jessie squinted at her, brows drawn as if she couldn't understand what Elsie was saying.

'Michael...' She wouldn't call him Dad. Not now. 'He said he was sorry but it was Annabelle's decision as it's her wealth that keeps them. He offered me money so we could rent a place but I refused it. It felt like he was paying me off somehow. Doing away with his guilt. I wasn't going to give him that satisfaction.'

'I'm so sorry,' Aunt Sarah said. 'I hoped there was a happy ending for you. I know how difficult Mother and Ada can be. And Leo is determined to have this room back.'

Elsie looked at Jessie. The younger girl pushed the suitcase off the bed. It landed on the floor with a loud thump.

'You should have taken the money,' Jessie said and there was a bitterness in her voice that Elsie had never heard before. She got up and ran out of the room.

'Leave her,' Aunt Sarah advised, when Elsie got up to go after her. 'She's upset but she'll calm down if you give her space.' She got up and placed the suitcase neatly under the table. 'What will you do now?'

'I don't know. We have a few months before Grand-mother evicts us. Something will turn up.' Elsie tried to sound cheerful.

Aunt Sarah pecked her cheek and left. Elsie sat staring at the small suitcase under the table. Poor Jessie. She had taken it badly. She decided not to go the knitting club that evening but to spend the time with her little sister. After their meal though, when she said as much, Jessie insisted that she go.

'I'm fine, so I am. I'll read my book and get to bed as usual. On you go.'

'If you're sure?'

'I said I was, didn't I? I'd like to be alone,' Jessie said tonelessly.

Elsie had no choice but to get wrapped up and head over to Doris's home but she couldn't help worrying about her sister.

—

It was a subdued meeting of the knitting club that evening. All three girls had a lot on their minds.

'Oh dear, we're awful quiet the night,' Doris remarked, setting her knitting down. She was working on a balaclava in army khaki.

'I'm sorry, I can't help worrying about Jessie. She took it really hard,' Elsie said, her fingers slipping a stitch again. It was going to be a holey sock for some RAF laddie if she didn't take more care.

'She's right about the money. You should have made him pay. I can't understand why you didn't. You and Jessie could have got away from your grandmother and rented a wee room for yourselves,' Annie said. She had Davey on her knee and wasn't even pretending to knit, although a half-finished yellow baby's jumper lay on the floor beside her.

'I wasn't going to take his pay-off,' Elsie said grimly.

'Do you want Mum to take Davey for you so you can knit?' Doris asked Annie.

Annie cuddled him in closer and shook her head. 'Not tonight. I can't be without him right now. I could have lost him when he was so sick.'

'Are you all right, Doris? You look a bit glum yourself,' Elsie said.

'Och, I'm fine really. It's just...' She poked at the unfortunate balaclava and then it all burst out of her. 'It's Roy. He's seeing this girl, Violet and I want to hate her but I can't 'cos she's so nice. Then I want to hate Roy but I can't do that either because I love him.' She stopped for a wheezy breath. 'Oh, God. It's my bloody asthma coming on.'

Elsie hunkered beside Doris's chair and put an arm round her. Annie shifted Davey onto her hip and leaned

231

over to squeeze Doris's hand. Doris managed a shaky laugh which ended in a cough.

'Breathe slowly,' Elsie said. 'That's it. In and out. Try and relax.'

'She can't, though,' Annie muttered. 'It's like me and Paul. It's impossible to relax when the man you love isn't talking to you.'

Doris blinked behind her thick specs. 'Roy isn't snubbing me. He's not around to snub. That's the problem. Him and that Violet are out and about so I never get to see him. His grandad reckons he'll come to his senses but I don't know. Mebbe Roy's hearing wedding bells.'

'Paul is angry with me and nothing I can say or do seems to put it right. As for Mum, she sniffs at me and waggles her eyebrows and won't say a word.'

'It can't last,' Elsie said. 'You've said sorry.'

'Aye, I know I have. How many times can I say it?' Annie said, gloomily.

Doris gripped both their hands so that the three of them were linked. 'We've got each other, girls, and we'll look after each other, so we will.'

–

A few days later, Jessie disappeared.

Elsie came back from a long shift at Fearnmore, the noise of the factory floor still ringing in her ears. It was long after six o'clock and she had missed the family's meal.

'Don't think I'm going to make you a hot meal now when tea finished a half hour ago,' Aunt Ada told her.

Isobel was sitting at the table, too. 'I'll take my coffee in the parlour, Sarah,' she announced, without a word of greeting to Elsie.

Aunt Sarah rushed to get the old woman's stick and help her up slowly.

'There's some vegetable pie in the cupboard,' Sarah said over her shoulder to Elsie. 'And custard for dessert. It's cold but you can heat it up.'

'Thanks. Where's Jessie?'

'Didn't she say she was visiting a friend after school today?'

Elsie remembered now that Sarah was right. It had flown out of her head what with the extra hours she'd had to put in for the war effort. They were all working longer these days and no one complained. There was a real camaraderie on the factory floor and she and Jeannie and Ruby and the rest of the girls sang popular songs above the noise of the machines and enjoyed *Workers' Playtime* in the canteen to keep them going.

Jessie had told her at breakfast as she shovelled in hot porridge at a rate that had Elsie frowning at her sister's table manners. She was glad that Jessie had finally found a friend to go and visit and hadn't thought to ask the girl's name or where she lived. Now she wished she had.

'It's not that late yet,' Sarah said, picking up on her concern.

'Aye, I'm probably worrying over nothing.'

'Do get a move on, Sarah,' Isobel snapped. 'I'm standing here waiting while you're holding a conversation. Help me into the parlour. I'm sure Elspeth doesn't need you but I do.'

The feeling of unease lingered even while she cleared up the dishes that Aunt Ada had left for her to wash, dry and put away. When it got dark just after seven p.m. and Jessie still wasn't home, Elsie couldn't wait any longer. She grabbed her coat and went outside. There was a thick, velvety blackness in Kiltie Street, with not a single light showing in the blackout. She listened out but there was no sound of a girl's footsteps. She ran back upstairs and knelt down to look under the bed. She had moved Jessie's cardboard suitcase from under the table so that they wouldn't have to look at it and be reminded of their father's betrayal. Now, the space under the bed was empty except for a crumpled piece of paper.

She ran out of the flat and along the street, avoiding obstacles more by luck than skill. She bumped into a couple of people, crying out an apology but rushing on, not waiting to be polite.

Fred opened the door to the railway cottage and she slipped inside to prevent the light seeping out to attract the ARP warden's angry shouts – or worse, a fine.

'Elsie, what is it?' Fred asked in surprise.

He was in his uniform and she wondered if he had returned from his shift or was about to start it.

'It's Jessie. I think she's run away from home.'

Monica Wiley appeared. She didn't seem surprised to see Elsie and ushered her into the parlour. 'Sit in here with Fred, love. Bert's out saving the world from Jerry with the Home Guard and I have to nip down and see young Mrs Berry who's expecting her fifth baby very soon. You'll be all right with our Fred.'

Elsie murmured her thanks but didn't really notice Fred's mum leaving.

'Are you going to work?' she asked Fred.

'No, that's me finished my shift. Give me a moment to change and I'll be right with you.'

He was as good as his word and came back a few minutes later dressed in dark trousers with a white shirt and green knitted jumper, his hair tousled.

'You look tired. I shouldn't have come to bother you.'

He smothered a yawn and grinned sheepishly. 'I was going to say I wasn't tired but obviously that would be a lie. It's these warehouse thefts. We're all on extra shifts, keeping our eyes peeled but whoever's responsible is elusive. Anyway, enough about that. What's all this about Jessie?'

'She's been so unhappy,' Elsie said. 'It's all this business with our father.' She told Fred about her return visit to Pladda Lane and Jessie's reaction to the bad news. 'She sounded so bitter when she said I should have taken his money. I tried to explain why I couldn't but she just turned away from me. I should have realised she might run away. She's been so quiet ever since.'

Fred's warm, capable hand covered hers. 'Now, don't go blaming yourself. That's not doing you or Jessie any good. Who is this friend she was visiting today?'

'That's just it. I don't think there is a friend. I think she made it up to give herself time to run away somewhere.'

'Where would she go? Think hard, Elsie.'

'I don't need to. I know where she's gone.' She handed him the letter she had found under the bed.

Fred smoothed it out and read in silence. The clock on the mantelpiece ticked methodically. He looked up when he had finished.

'Where do the Cranstons live?'

'They live outside a village in Perthshire. Jessie was evacuated to them. I had no idea that they were writing to her and sending her pocket money. She never told me.'

'Looks like she's been saving it up to get a train fare,' Fred said.

Elsie jumped up. 'I've got to go to the station.'

Fred stood up too. 'It's no use going tonight. There won't be a train running at this hour. We'll go in the morning. First train over.'

'Don't you have to work?'

'As it happens, I've got a day off tomorrow. Come on, I'll walk you home and then we can meet at Central Station in the morning.'

'Thanks, Fred. You're a good friend.'

He put his arm around her and Elsie felt the strength of his lean body. He only meant to be friendly but it was doing strange things to her. He moved away as if he knew what she felt. She flushed. What must he think of her? But when she dared to glance up he was busy fetching a coat and hadn't noticed anything.

'It's a nice night for a wander,' he smiled. 'You mustn't worry about Jessie. We'll get her home safe and sound.'

–

The first train to Perth left early in the morning and Elsie and Fred were on it. She watched the countryside speeding by the train window.

'Jessie had all day to get over there. I'll bet she didn't go to school at all,' she said.

'She'll be safe with the Cranstons,' Fred said. 'From what you've told me, they're good folks.'

'Yes, she called them Auntie Alison and Uncle Donald. I wish I'd listened more to her stories of staying there. I didn't realise how close she'd become to them.'

It was a minor miracle that the train wasn't stopped or delayed or shunted into sidings for hours. In fact, it wasn't very busy at all. There were some servicemen and women and a family sitting near them. The mother held a bag with a live chicken in it. The children kept petting the bird and she slapped at their hands and tried to prevent the chicken from escaping. It was all very amusing and helped to pass the time. Fred winked at Elsie and she had to smother her smiles.

–

Elsie had forgotten how reclusive the Cranstons' lovely house was. The woodland was flecked with green and yellow, a hint of early autumn colours. She stopped at the entrance pillars, their grey stone brightened by tiny mosses. The path wound round the bend and out of sight. In the nearby fields, the cows mooed and there was birdsong.

'Is this it?' Fred asked.

Elsie nodded. She had a strange feeling that when she stepped onto the path between the pillars that there would be no going back. It was only four months since she had fetched Jessie home to Kiltic Street and Louise but it felt much, much longer. Fred was waiting patiently and she smiled up at him and walked on.

Mrs Potter answered the grand door with a kindly smile which slipped a little when she saw who it was.

'Is she here?' Elsie said.

'Yes, dear. She's here and safe. Do come in and I'll call Mrs Cranston.' The housekeeper emphasised the word 'safe' and Elsie knew what she was being told. That she should never have taken Jessie away from this place to the big city with all its dangers.

She and Fred were ushered into the same room she'd been taken to before on her last visit. They stood in the middle of it, although they had been offered seats.

'I'm that fidgety, I can't sit,' Elsie explained. 'I have to see her before I can rest.'

'We know she's here so that's a relief. No missing child to seek,' Fred said, and Elsie remembered that he was a policeman. Of course, he had been thinking about what to do if Jessie hadn't turned up. Elsie hadn't got that far in her own thoughts. Thank goodness Jessie had had the sense to come here to safety.

'Miss Weir.' Alison Cranston came into the room quietly.

'Where is she? Please?'

'Of course. You don't need to worry. Jessie is quite safe. She turned up yesterday and I insisted that she write to you straight away to let you know where she was. But you won't have received the letter yet.'

'I have to see her.'

Fred placed a warning hand on her agitated arm but Elsie pushed it off. He couldn't understand. She was Jessie's sister but in a way she had replaced their mother in having responsibility for her.

Jessie came in, her expression unsure. Elsie ran to her and hugged her tightly. Jessie hesitated then returned the pressure until Elsie pulled back and slapped her in the face.

'That's for running off. How could you! I've been that afraid.'

'I'm sorry.' Jessie rubbed her reddened cheek. 'I deserved that but I'm not going back, whatever you say. Uncle Donald and Auntie Alison say that I can stay here until the war's done.'

Elsie looked at Alison Cranston who had the grace to look embarrassed. Mrs Potter arrived in with a tea tray at that moment which took the tension out of the room. Elsie watched Jessie happily help the older woman to set down the cups and saucers and adjust the knitted tea cosy on the teapot. She had to admit that her sister looked right at home in spite of the posh surroundings which made Elsie herself feel like the proverbial fish out of water.

Donald Cranston joined them. He had a pipe which he chewed at, letting coils of smoke escape from the side of his mouth whenever he spoke. He offered Fred and Elsie cigarettes which they both refused politely.

'I'm not quite sure where to begin.' Alison Cranston looked at them all.

'She's my sister. She belongs with me,' Elsie cried.

'Why don't we hear what Mr and Mrs Cranston have to say,' Fred said.

'May I ask who you are?' Donald Cranston asked, the blue smoke coiling sideways from his mouth and up towards the room's high ceiling.

'I'm Fred Cooper, a friend of the family and I'm also the local policeman. Elsie came to see me yesterday when she found that Jessie was missing.'

Elsie was proud of Fred. He sounded confident and in control. He probably had to talk to lots of people in his line of work, and he wasn't letting the wealthy surroundings daunt him the way they did her.

Donald Cranston nodded amiably as if that all made sense. 'Jessie won't come to any harm with us, Mr Cooper. I'm sure Elsie will have explained that we have given her a home with us for over two years and we would love to be allowed to continue to do so.'

'You gave her the money to come here,' Elsie blurted out. She found that hard to forgive.

Donald Cranston's eyebrows rose as he turned to Jessie. 'Didn't you tell your sister that I sent you pocket money? That was wrong of you.'

Jessie looked ashamed but Elsie had the most curious sensation watching them. It was as if she was watching a gentle father chastise his daughter in a loving way. Jessie wasn't afraid of him but clearly wanted his approval. It was such a terrible pity that her own father had never been there for her.

'I saved it up in wee bits. I'm sorry, Elsie, but if I'd told you, you'd never have let me come here.'

That was true. There was nothing Elsie could say to that.

'Come along and see the bicycle Auntie Alison and I got for you. We were going to give it to you back in May but you left so suddenly we never had the opportunity.' Donald Cranston snuffed out his pipe and left it in a dish on a side table before waving Jessie out in front of him.

'I'll go and see it, too.' Fred got up before Elsie could stop him and followed the other two out.

She was left with Alison Cranston.

'That wasn't very subtle, I do apologise, but Donald knew I wanted to speak to you on your own,' Alison said.

'Fred must've had an inkling of that too,' Elsie said wryly.

Alison surprised her by smiling. It softened her rather plain features and made her eyes twinkle. No wonder Jessie loved being here. The Cranstons were nice people.

'Please let her stay. She is safe here from bombing, we have more food than you do in the city with the farms nearby. She's too thin. Mrs Potter will soon feed her up. But above all, let her stay because we love her and will look after her.'

'I love her too.'

'I know and we will send her back to you when this awful war is over, I promise you.'

There was nothing more to be said. Elsie had known from the second that she stepped past the entrance pillars how it would turn out. In a way, it was the right outcome.

Jessie was ecstatic at the news and now Elsie wouldn't worry about her sister's unhappiness in the top floor flat at number one, Kiltie Street. She and Fred left to get the last train back to Glasgow although the Cranstons and Jessie had begged them to stay the night. She let him hold her hand, the gentle squeezing of his fingers a comfort and support as they walked back to the village.

Fred didn't let his inward emotions show as he guided Elsie back to the station. He was reluctant to let go of her hand but knew that he should. He thought of how he had hugged her when she came to say that Jessie was missing. He had had to let go, afraid that his body would betray him. She had felt so right in his embrace. Her hair had tickled his chin; it was soft and scented and he had wanted her suddenly. Now he was confused. He liked Annie. Safe Annie whom he could never have but could admire from a distance. Elsie was different. She was single and it wouldn't do. Alice had burnt him and he had nothing to offer another woman. He wasn't about to let his heart be broken a second time.

# Chapter Seventeen

'Where is your sister?'

Elsie had been called in by Sarah to speak to Isobel Mearns. The old woman sat stiffly in her armchair, one gnarled hand resting on her walking stick. On the small table beside her was a bottle of Milk of Magnesia, only a third of the liquid left. Sarah fussed about with a damp cloth, wiping up spilled droplets and picking up the sticky spoon until Isobel waved her away irritably.

'Well?' she snapped, when Elsie didn't immediately answer. 'The girl is my responsibility, after all. I deserve to know if she has been removed from my house.'

For a moment, Elsie thought that her grandmother actually cared. Perhaps she had softened towards them, even loved them.

'What will people think?'

'Is that all that matters?' Elsie said, realising her mistake. This wasn't about love from Isobel. 'Don't you want to know if Jessie is safe and well and whether she's happy?'

'Enough of your impudence. I have a duty to care for you now that Louise is dead. They may say many things about me but not that I don't do right by my family.'

Elsie gave up. Her grandmother wasn't going to change. 'Jessie has gone back to live with the Cranstons in Perthshire. She'll be safe there until the war's over.'

Isobel gave a small nod of acknowledgement then winced. Elsie knew she should feel sympathy as her arthritic joints were obviously paining her. But it was hard to care when there wasn't an ounce of affection from her grandmother. She walked out of the room and found Sarah hovering outside the door.

'Don't be too hard on her. She's having one of her bad days. The pain is awful, you know and the medicine doesn't really stop it.'

Elsie couldn't bring herself to answer. She brushed past her aunt and went into her room and closed the door. Aunt Sarah's kindness had made this place bearable but she was blinkered when it came to Isobel. She refused to see how mean and cold her mother was to Elsie and Jessie. There was always an excuse to be made.

There was a letter on the bed. It must have come in the post that day. Elsie had come home from the factory and been pulled in to speak to Isobel before she barely had her coat off. Now, she sank down onto the blanket, feeling its familiar softness. She kicked off her shoes and felt the lumpy ridges of the rag rug under her curled toes. This was the only home she had and there were some small comforts to be had. The smell of cabbage cooking was good, too. She was hungry as usual.

She tore open the envelope and slid out the letter. It was another from Aunt Norah. Aunt Norah's first letter had been like a story book, it was so entertaining, so she curled up to read this one with a pleasant sense of anticipation. This letter was full of tales of her work at the munitions factory in Manchester and her evenings as a fire watcher on the top of the building. Despite being almost forty-six, she appeared to be full of energy and working all hours that God gave. She described walks with

Felicity in the countryside and told Elsie about their little dog Chopin and the new tricks he had learnt.

> *Felicity asks kindly after you, too. We wondered if you and Jessie might consider moving south to live with us? We have enough room here as we rattle about downstairs mostly. The lodger has one bedroom and there is a spare which would be quite suitable. Please think about it. We would love to see you both.*
> *Your loving Aunt Norah.*

And there it was. Elsie giggled until she had to smother her face in her pillow. Only it wasn't happy laughter. It was a mild hysteria which she got under control by sneezing at the goose feathers escaping from the cotton pillowslip. Hadn't she dreamed of Aunt Norah offering them a home? She had begun to write to her in the hope of building a relationship so that eventually she might ask if they could live with Aunt Norah and Felicity if it didn't work out with Michael. Now it was too late. There was no way she could leave Scotland without Jessie.

–

On the last Saturday of October, Doris spread out the newspapers on the table. It was Halloween the next day and the weather was cold, damp and dark, with night coming in fast despite daylight saving time. She rubbed her lenses clear and hunched over the headlines. '*Red Army Racing to Close Gap,*' she read. '*Russian forces have pushed on another seven and a half to fifteen miles in pursuit of the retreating Germans south-east of the Lower Dnieper, where the fourth Ukrainian army is smashing its way through to one of the great victories of the war.'*

It was thrilling, although as she cast her eyes over the rest of the front page, it was clear that the war was being fought all over the globe and with varying fortunes. Where was Lower Dnieper? She opened her mouth to ask Roy and remembered where she was. Not at Roy's cramped, noisy home with his cheerful face and shared fascination with the war news but at her own, with her mum stirring something on the range. She missed Roy something terrible. She missed his grandad too, and his cheeky remarks. She even missed the noise and bother of Roy's wee brothers and Christine racing around creating havoc.

As if her mum could read her thoughts, Leila looked over. 'Why are you reading that here, love? Have you fallen out with Roy?'

'No, Mum. I haven't had an argument or anything like that. It's just… well, Roy's got Violet now.'

'I thought you told me her unit got moved down south?'

'Aye, I did and she has gone but maybe Roy's hankering after her still.'

'Was it serious then?' Leila's wooden spoon was poised over the pan as she waited for Doris's answer.

Doris sighed. She took off her specs and inspected them. She turned large brown eyes to her mother. 'I don't know, Mum. But he seemed awful fond of her.'

'Och well, he's bound to miss her then,' Leila said blithely, unaware of Doris's tender emotions. 'Here, come and taste this for me.'

'What is it?' Doris asked, suppressing another sigh. She had to forget about Roy Allen. She hadn't been over the last few Saturday afternoons and if he missed her, he hadn't shown it by seeking her out to ask why she wasn't turning up. No, he must be so upset, what with Violet going, that he wasn't even thinking about Doris.

'Mrs Morris passed me on a recipe for potato soup. I've cut up the tatties, sliced a wee bit of onion that I kept from last week and browned it in a little dripping and simmered it up. I'll make some dumplings to go with it as I've got flour left and they only need a wee teaspoon of baking powder and another of dried herbs to make the dough.'

'It's nice,' Doris said, not really tasting it, her thoughts on Roy.

She went back to her newspaper and Leila followed her, reading over her shoulder.

'That's a blow,' she said, pointing to an article on coal and reading it out loud. '*New coal restrictions come into operation on Monday. Most people will patriotically make do, we believe, with the thirteen cwt which is to be the maximum household allowance for the next two months. But, in Glasgow, it seems, coal merchants are far from sure that this amount will be available.*' She frowned and shook her head. 'Och, that's a worry. We can hardly manage on the allowance they give us now. What will we do?'

'I'm sure we'll be fine, Mum. Let's not worry until it happens. At least we're allowed one packet of dried eggs per ration book every four weeks if you read that wee part of the paper.'

That seemed to cheer Leila up. She paused on her way back to the potato soup, which bubbled in the pan.

'How would you feel if we left Kiltie Street?' she asked.

Doris was so shocked she forgot to turn onto the next page of the papers. 'Why would we do that?'

'It's that Mr Gibb. I've not enjoyed my own wee garden all year for fear of seeing him. And when I do meet him, he stares at me. I can't take it any more.'

Leave Kiltie Street, Doris thought in dismay. She couldn't imagine living anywhere else. She would miss Elsie and Annie and all their neighbours. She wouldn't be living next door to Roy and the rest of the Allen family. She looked at her mum.

'I don't know.'

'I want you to think about it. I don't need an answer right now but we'll talk about it soon.'

—

Ivy cut off the crust on the bread and handed it to Davey. He chewed and dribbled, a bright spot of red on his cheek.

'He's teething, poor wee man,' she said. 'He'll be cranky with it.'

Annie picked him up from his blanket on the floor and cradled him. 'He can cry all he wants. I don't mind. I'll sing him his favourite song.'

'And what might that be?'

'He loves "Roses of Picardy". Funny that. It's sort of sad but he likes that better than a lullaby. He perked right up when we heard Richard Crooks sing it on the wireless.'

'He's got good taste, our wee lad, I'll give him that. I love that song myself.' Ivy smiled at Annie.

'What's your favourite?' Annie asked, seizing this moment of harmony with her mum.

They had managed to put the events of their visit to Dumbarton and Davey's illness behind them but their relationship hadn't quite recovered. These days Annie felt like she was walking on eggshells, trying to please Ivy and not getting there. Gone were the times when she was annoyed with her mum and wishing she didn't visit. Now she was desperate to be back in her good books.

'Oh, let's see. I love The Andrews Sisters singing "Don't Sit Under the Apple Tree" or "Roll Out the Barrel" and I'm fond of George Formby and "When I'm Cleaning Windows". But it's got to be Vera Lynn's "We'll Meet Again".'

Ivy started to sing it and Annie joined in. Davey clapped his hands together and crooned too until the two women laughed. He grinned up at them, showing a tiny ridge of white in his lower gum.

'There it is. His first tooth's coming through, all right,' Ivy said proudly.

'You're right, Mum. Davey, you're a clever lad, so you are.'

'Aye, count your blessings, love. You've got more than you know.'

'I do know, Mum. I do.' Annie blinked. Was her mother never going to let her forget? But when she glanced over, Ivy was humming and smiling, her beetling black eyebrows for once calm and straight. Maybe, just maybe, it was all going to be fine.

The door slammed and she jumped. Paul was home.

'Can he no' just come in quietly like normal folk?' Ivy complained.

The bond between Annie's husband and his mother-in-law hadn't lasted.

'He's tired, is all.'

'Aye, and why is that? Because of the funny hours and other funny whatnots he's up to,' Ivy said darkly.

Paul had avoided the kitchen and gone straight into their bedroom and shut the door. Annie wanted to leave him to it but she knew her marriage couldn't take much more silence and argument.

'You hungry?' she said, sticking her head round the door.

'I'll get something later.' Paul lay on the bed, staring at the ceiling.

'Fine. Suit yourself.' She shut the door hard. She was shaking but she wasn't sure if it was anger or fear. The gap between them was lengthening and she didn't know how to make it right.

—

In the bedroom, Paul lay and counted the cracks in the ceiling. There were a few. It needed a lick of paint but there wasn't any to be had and he was too tired to paint even if he had had a pot of it. He heard Annie thumping about and felt guilty. She thought he still blamed her for Davey's sickness but that wasn't the truth. He had forgiven her almost immediately but he hadn't forgiven himself for not being there to look after her and the wean, both of them. What kind of husband and father lay in a drunken stupor all night unaware of Annie's friend knocking on the door and not knowing where his wife and child were until morning? He'd got such a fright waking up with a blinding headache and finding them gone. He loved them so much but somehow these days he couldn't show it.

It was Archie Bale's fault. He had Paul working all sorts of hours and when Paul had said he was going to find other work, Archie had reminded him of the debts he owed. He had borrowed a wee bit of money from Archie to buy food and pay rent and it had been a mistake he wasn't allowed to forget.

It was better to keep Annie at bay. That way he wouldn't have to tell her all the dishonest jobs Archie had him doing. What she didn't know couldn't hurt her. She was happy with the money coming in and he was pleased to see her sing and chat to Davey, content that he was providing for them. The trouble was, the cost was rising.

Archie had decided it wasn't enough to sell on goods on the black market that he received from others. He reckoned there was more money to be made by 'liberating' the goods directly. Their one previous attempt hadn't worked but that, it seemed, hadn't put him off the notion.

'What does that mean?' Paul had asked.

'It means, pal, that you and me are going to carry out a wee job. I've got a man watching the warehouses along the canal. He tips me the wink when the goods come in and then we'll help ourselves. You cannae drive a truck so I'll drive but I don't trust anyone else to come with me to get the stuff. Even with one arm, you can shift enough boxes.'

'There are night watchmen. How you gonnae get past them?' Paul asked.

It wasn't as if he was an angel himself. He'd poached salmon and game from the countryside around Clydebank, growing up with his brothers. He had sold ciggies and booze that had fallen off the back of a lorry. He was pretty sure he had passed black market goods and dirty money to and fro in Archie's mysterious parcels. But this was on a new level. If they were caught, they'd be doing prison time with hard labour.

'I'll find a way to deal with the security.' Archie grinned. 'No thinking of bailing on me, are you? Cos if you are, I'll remind you that I know where you live and that I've met that pretty wifey of yours. Does Annie know you owe me money?'

'Your timing's off. The polis are all over the place like fleas on a scabby dug because of the thefts from warehouses recently.'

'Ah, that's where yer wrong. A warehouse got done on the canal a while ago but others by the docks since. The polis are no' looking at the canal the now. It's perfect timing. Leave the thinking to me,' Archie sneered.

Archie's words echoed in his head as Paul lay on the bed. His missing arm ached, the pains shooting right into his non-existent fingertips. He rubbed the stump until it stopped. He heard Ivy murmur something in the kitchen and then her and Annie laughing. They were homely sounds and made him vividly aware of all he had to lose.

'After Halloween. Be ready,' Archie had warned.

# Chapter Eighteen

Doris was having a terrible day. It had started at Franny's shop when a customer had requested Vida elastic and been argumentative when told there was none to be had. Doris reminded her of all the adverts showing goods that were unavailable until after the war but the woman had been quite rude until Franny bustled over to calm her down with soothing, polite promises that she'd be the first to know when the elastic came back in.

In the afternoon, Doris had broken a small figurine while dusting in Isobel Mearns' parlour and received a furious dressing-down and a docking of her wage. Miserable from that, she came home to see Mr Gibb had separated his part of the back court by placing large stones in a line to the Anderson shelter. He had also removed the Connellys' belongings from the shelter. Leila's bench and blankets, their oil lamp and box of tallow candles were sitting outside. When she looked inside the Andie, Doris saw he had filled it with plant pots and gardening tools so that if, God forbid, there was more bombing, they would have trouble getting inside in a hurry.

She knew she ought to confront him or, at the very least, take all his stuff back out of the corrugated metal shelter. Instead, she went into their flat, anger burning impotently in her chest. She couldn't tell her mum. It would likely be the last straw and Doris was already terrified that Leila would give up the rent on the Kiltie Street rooms without telling her.

So it was with a heavy heart that she trekked out of her home after the evening meal to follow Roy along the road and up onto the canal path. Night had fallen and Leila had muttered about the factory taking advantage of her and to be careful walking home but she ignored that. Even if Roy and Violet were an item, Doris couldn't give him up so easily. She stumbled over the struts in the close and almost fell onto the brick of the baffle wall, grazing her knuckles.

'Can the day get any worse?' she grumbled, licking her knuckles and feeling them sting.

She followed the sound of Roy's cheerful whistling and the hard clicking of his soles on the cobbles. Why was she torturing herself like this? She had always enjoyed seeing Roy to the warehouses, occasionally catching him up for a chat. He always looked pleased to see her and she had a sneaking suspicion he knew she followed him to his work. Still, he wouldn't be expecting it this late in the year and she had no intention of running to meet him tonight. If he wanted her, he knew where she lived. If he missed their Saturday afternoons all he had to do was ask her to come over.

Roy left the road and started up the grassy bank to join the canal towpath. She smelled the mixed aromas of rubber, coal and chemicals that hung over the canal in a miasma from the various factories along its length. The working day was done but the smells lingered. She hung back, knowing his route to the warehouses. There was a full moon shining onto the murky water and illuminating the towpath and the outlines of the buildings.

The biting, cold air helped dissipate her anger and unhappiness. She enjoyed looking at the water and the silvery ripples as a swan swam past on its oily surface. She decided to turn back. The walk had done her good and she decided she might visit Roy the following Saturday. They could be friends again. Violet didn't have to come between them.

Just as she turned to go home, a movement further along the canal caught her attention. It wasn't Roy. He had gone inside the warehouse office, a small whitewashed cottage beside the warehouses. Frowning, she stared into the dark trying to make out what was going on. In spite of the bright moonlight, it was difficult to identify the shapes in the shadows.

She walked towards the warehouses. There was a grove of trees on the way and she hid behind the trunk of the furthest tree and peeped out carefully. What she saw made her gasp. Two men were walking towards the cottage. They were taller than either Roy or Hugh and from the way they acted, Doris knew instinctively that they were up to no good.

The two figures went straight into the cottage. Doris's breath caught. Roy and Hugh were in there. What was going on? A long few minutes passed in which she felt her nerves tighten. Somehow she couldn't move. What should she do? What were *they* doing? She was suddenly afraid.

As she continued to watch, the figures, clear in the moonlight, came back outside and one of them leaned towards the cottage door. What was he doing? She screwed up her eyes. He stood upright and his arm jerked. Was he throwing something away? Then they slid like shadows into the adjacent warehouse.

When Roy and Hugh didn't appear to chase the two men, Doris realised what must have happened. The intruders had locked the office door and thrown away the key. They must be intent on stealing from the warehouses. She was all alone on the canal path. No one else was around to help. It was up to her. She had to let Roy and Hugh out. But could she do it before the men came back out of the warehouse and saw her?

'I can't do this, I'm scared,' she whispered, all her fears and insecurities surfacing. She could almost hear her mum's voice telling her to run away. Telling her she wasn't strong enough or good enough to do this.

But Roy was in there, possibly in danger. What had those men done to him and old Hugh?

'Hang on, Roy. I'm coming,' Doris cried, releasing her grip on the tree's bark and taking a faltering step along the path.

There was no time for second thoughts. If she was to find the key and release Roy, she had to move fast. Doris ran along the path, at every moment expecting a sinister figure to emerge from the warehouse door and find her. She reached the office and knelt on the damp grass, spreading her hands out in front of her, desperately trying to find the key.

She kept glancing at the warehouse so close by as her fingers scrabbled in the grass. And there it was. The cold, rough metal of the key. Thankfully, she picked it up. By now, her heart was hammering and she felt sick with tension.

Mum's right. I am timid and I'm not cut out for courage, she thought.

That didn't stop her from fumbling the key into the lock and turning it. Praying that the office door didn't creak, she pushed the handle and opened the door. Inside, Roy and Hugh were tied to their chairs. Their faces were white ovals as they looked to her. They both had rags stuffed in their mouths.

She ran to Roy and pulled the rag out. Beside him, old Hugh was moaning and writhing in his chair.

'Untie me,' Roy said in a low, urgent voice. His hands were tied behind the chair.

She tried but the knot was tight. 'I can't,' she said and there was a distinct wobble in her voice.

'It's all right, Dor. You've got this. On the table, there's Hugh's knife he uses for his baccy. Grab that and saw through the rope.'

She found the knife and managed to cut Roy's hands free.

He leapt up and grabbed her shoulders. 'Listen, Dor. I'll free Hugh. You go for help. Run as fast as you can and don't stop.'

'But…' She didn't get to finish her sentence as Roy kissed her hard on the lips.

'You're a brave girl, Doris Connelly. Now go and don't look back!'

All the way back, she felt a prickling on her spine between her shoulder blades; she was certain that the bad men would come out and chase her. She imagined them catching her and throwing her in the canal so she couldn't be a witness to their crimes. She also realised that she'd recognised one of them. The man who had thrown the key. There had been something odd about his arms. She was sure now that it was Paul Thom, Annie's husband.

Above all, she felt the warm delicious sensation of Roy's mouth pressing on hers. He had kissed her. It was in the height of danger and he wasn't thinking clearly, she told herself as her breath came faster. But oh, how lovely the kiss had been.

–

Annie paced her kitchen. Something was wrong, she felt it in her water, as Ivy would say. It wasn't Davey. He was fine, fast asleep in the bedroom. No, it was Paul.

That morning he had eaten his breakfast in silence, as usual. She had almost forgotten the days early on in their marriage when they had laughed and talked together in the morning before he left for war. After breakfast he surprised her by coming up behind her as she put the dishes into the sink and hugging her. She turned in his embrace and he kissed her fiercely.

'I love you,' he said. 'I'm sorry I haven't told you that recently. I'm sorry for a lot of things.'

'I love you too,' she told him. 'What's happened to us, Paul? We're so... so very far apart these days.'

Paul nodded. 'I know. It's my fault. I cannae explain it but I want you to know if anything happens to me that I never meant to harm you.'

'Nothing's going to happen to you,' she said. 'You're back from the war. You're safe with me and Davey.'

He grimaced. 'I've seen and done terrible things, Annie. Out there.'

'Tell me about them. It'll help to get it all out and I want to know. You've been awfy distant since you came back. I want us to be close again like we used to be. So, tell me.'

'Not now. I want to forget it. I want to move on.'

She doubted that was possible without letting it out – like lancing a boil – but she also knew that it was impossible to get Paul to change his mind if he was set on something.

'All right. We'll talk later,' she said, unwilling to give up entirely.

He winced and swore and she looked at him questioningly.

'It's this arm of mine. It's bloody sore aw the time.' He raised the stump of his arm.

'How can that be? It's not there.'

'I don't know but it's real all the same.'

She saw the grooved lines either side of his mouth and realised how he had been suffering.

'Oh, Paul. Why didn't you tell me this earlier? I'll ask Doctor Graham to come and see you. Maybe he can explain it and give you something for the pain.'

Paul grunted. Annie wiped her hands on the cloth beside the sink and managed a bright smile.

'Are you away out or do ye fancy another cuppa and a wee blether?'

'Aye, that would be nice. I'm no' out 'til tonight.'

They spent a pleasant day together, Paul helping to change Davey, playing with him and singing him songs. It squeezed Annie's heart to see his big, strong hand over Davey's soft baby hands helping him to clap in time to the songs' rhythms. He had the knack now of swooping the baby up in his good arm and using his other to steady him.

But as the evening drew on, she noticed his tension rising. He ate his meal quietly. There was an eggless sponge pudding for afters which she'd spent two hours steaming and served with a tiny dollop of blackberry jam but he didn't comment on it.

'Did you enjoy that?' she said finally as he pushed his plate aside.

'What?'

'The pudding. You've not finished it.'

He pushed it over to her. 'I'm not that hungry the night. You have it. I've got to go out.'

'It's Archie, isn't it? He's got you on some job. It can't be respectable if you're away out into the dark night to do it. Stay with me, please, Paul.'

'I can't.' He moved abruptly, his words flat and she knew he was lost to it.

She heard him pull his jacket off the rickety coat stand and the front door closing.

Sitting in the kitchen with the oil lamp flickering, his earlier words came back to her. She stood up and walked back and forth. *If anything happens to me...* What did he mean? Suddenly, she couldn't stay there any longer. Paul was out working for Archie and whatever he was doing, it must be dangerous. He was warning her that he might not come back.

'What have you done?' she muttered, picking up the sleeping Davey and wrapping him in his blanket.

She went out of their flat at number six, holding Davey tight to her chest. She felt her way round the baffle wall, its rough brick scraping her fingers and hitting her shoulder painfully as she hurried round it. The damp night air smelt of coal smoke and rotting drains. She walked swiftly to the end of Kiltie Street where the first tenement was. Outside the ground floor flat, she paused. She needed either Doris or Elsie. Then she was climbing the stone stairs. Elsie would know what to do. Doris would be afraid and Mrs Connelly would set her off further.

Ada Mearns was all for not letting her in. 'We are eating our evening meal. It's a most inconvenient time to be calling.'

'I'm sorry but I have to see Elsie.'

Ada's stern features hardened. 'That won't be possible. Come back tomorrow.'

'Elsie!' Annie shocked herself and the thin, severe woman in front of her by bellowing out her friend's name.

With relief, she saw Elsie appear behind Ada.

'Thank you, Aunt Ada. Annie, come away into my room and we can talk.'

The two young women hurried into Elsie's room and shut the door on Ada's affronted figure.

Elsie gave a snort of laughter. 'It's not often someone gets the better of Aunt Ada but well done, Annie, you managed it.'

On another visit, Annie would have enjoyed a giggle about that but her fears overrode any idea of fun. Elsie's smile faded.

'What's the matter? Here, let me take Davey, you look fit to drop.'

'It's Paul. He's in danger. I'm sure of it. He's gone out on a job for Archie Bale but it was different tonight. The way he was talking, it was like he knew he wasn't coming back. I'm sure Archie's got him in over his head. I'm so worried. And I found this.' She scrabbled in her pocket and gave Elsie a scrap of paper.

Elsie sat for a moment looking at it and chewing on her lip until Annie wanted to scream. Instead, she made herself wait. What else could she do? Running out into the night after Paul by herself wasn't going to work.

'This is a sketch of the warehouses up at the canal,' Elsie said. 'Where did you get it?'

'It was on the floor under the coat stand. It must've fallen out of Paul's pocket when he went out. I'm worried that's where he and Archie are headed. What if Archie's intending to break into them?'

'Take Davey and go home,' Elsie said. 'You can't do anything with a wee baby to look after. I'll see what I can find out.'

'How are you going to do that?' Annie asked, but Elsie shook her head and shooed her out the door.

There was nothing to be done except go home with Elsie's reassurance that as soon as she found something, she'd let Annie know.

–

Once Annie had gone, Elsie raced downstairs and hammered on Doris's front door. Leila Connelly answered it.

'Is Doris in?' Elsie was inside and glancing around before Leila had answered.

'She's out at her factory shift. What's wrong?'

Knowing what Doris's mum was like, Elsie forced a smile to her face. 'Och, nothing at all. I wanted to borrow a dress from her, that was all. So, she's at Fearnmore, is that right?'

Leila nodded. 'She'll be back soon if you want to wait for her.'

'I'll catch her tomorrow.'

Elsie went back upstairs to fetch her torch and then went out and down onto the street. She knew exactly where Doris was and it certainly wasn't the Fearnmore munitions factory. She had told Elsie about her Wednesday evening walks and Roy Allen. Elsie bet that was where she was right now. She just had one detour to make before trying to find her friend.

Soon, she was scrambling up the grassy bank from the road onto the canal path. She didn't need her torch as the moonlight was so bright it cast her shadow onto the ground in front of her. Surely that would make finding Doris easy? Elsie glanced ahead and thought she saw a shape down low. It was hard to make out, but she could see something near to a grove of trees which were almost black beside the water. Beyond that were the warehouses, vaguely outlined.

She didn't want to get too close to the warehouses in case Archie Bale was there. He was a nasty sort who, she was sure, wouldn't quail at violence if he was seen breaking in. She shivered. She had to warn Doris to keep well clear of Roy and the warehouse area. What about Roy and old Hugh? Were they all right?

All these thoughts tumbled through her brain and she almost tripped over the crouching figure on the towpath.

'Doris, is that you?'

Doris was straining to catch her breath. She couldn't speak. Her breath rasped as she pointed a shaky finger back towards the warehouses.

'It's all right,' Elsie said, helping her friend up. 'Help is on its way.'

Doris struggled with her and managed to get free. 'Need... to get... police,' she whispered with agitation. Her voice was gritty and raw and she swallowed a great gulp of air before coughing.

'I went to see Fred before I found you. He's coming as soon as he's raised the alarm. We need to get out of here. Can you walk? Here, I'll hook my arm in yours. Try to breathe calmly. That's it.'

Elsie kept up a low chatter as she tried to pull Doris away from the area of the warehouses. She glanced over her shoulder as they moved crab–like from the scene. With every step she felt a sense of relief as the dark shapes grew smaller behind them.

'Fred says it could be that Archie Bale's got Paul involved in breaking into the warehouses. He says the police have been on extra shifts at the docks expecting a break-in there. Annie's warning has come at the right moment. They weren't keeping an eye on the canal at all. She found a scrap of paper, see, with the warehouses marked and arrows in and out.'

They almost tumbled down the grassy bank onto the road and Elsie grabbed Doris. Her friend's breathing had eased a little and it was a relief to be on the flat surface, shiny black in the drizzle and moonlight.

'What will happen to Paul?' Doris wheezed, her pale face turned to Elsie. Her spectacles were misted up and her mouth a circle of sadness. 'Poor Annie.'

'Whatever happens, we'll be there for her.'

Behind them came the sound of police whistles and when they craned their necks back towards the canal, they saw distant bobbing lights. There came faint shouts and the rumbling of an engine. In all the confusion, Elsie led Doris back to Kiltie Street and safety. She sent up a prayer that Roy and Hugh were unharmed and safe.

–

Fred Cooper appeared at Annie's door the next morning. She was heaping the dirty clothes in a pile ready to go to the wash house. Her nerves were spangling. Paul was still in bed asleep. He had slipped in the evening before, his face streaked with coal dust. He wouldn't answer any of her questions. She watched him clean his face and noted a pulse throbbing in his neck. He had gone to bed before her and when she had bathed Davey and put him in a fresh nappy and pyjamas and tucked him into the cot, Paul was snoring, dead to the world.

'I thought I'd come and check in on you,' Fred said, standing in the tiny hall opposite her. 'There was an incident up on the canal last night and no doubt the residents of Kiltie Street will hear about it and speculate so I'm doing the rounds to see if anyone saw anything and to put everyone's minds at rest.'

'What sort of incident?' Annie asked innocently. Inside, her guts were churning. What had Paul done?

'An attempted break-in at the warehouses. Luckily no one was seriously hurt although the two night watchmen were tied up and locked into their office and received a couple of blows to the head in the struggle. Your friend Doris was a real heroine; she managed to unlock the door and untie them. The night watchmen chased the culprit and we caught him.'

'Was it just the one thief?' Annie said, wondering if she ought to invite Fred into the kitchen. Beyond him, she saw the bedroom door open slightly and Paul in the shadows behind it, listening.

'Hugh, the night watchman, claims he saw two figures but apparently he's been having headaches and double-vision problems and his colleague is adamant that there was only the one thief.'

'Who is it?' Annie asked, although she knew the answer already. She just wanted it confirmed that he had got what he deserved.

'We nabbed a local man, Archie Bale. He's a known rogue. Looks like he's been planning this for a while although we don't believe he was involved with the previous thefts at the docks. He had loaded his truck with coal and bolts of cloth, some tinned stuffs, stolen petrol coupons – I'd guess for the truck. Oh, yes, Mr Dale's going away for a long stint on a number of charges.'

'Has he confessed?' Annie said, wondering whether Archie had grassed Paul up.

'Singing like the proverbial canary,' Fred grinned. 'Blaming everyone and their granny but no one's taking him seriously.'

Annie tried not to look towards Paul hiding behind the bedroom door. She kept her gaze on Fred or on her own, fidgety, hands.

'Well, I'd better get on with the washing, if that's all. You'll be busy if you're visiting the whole street this morning,' she said as cheerfully as possible, as if nothing was amiss.

'Is Mr Thom here?' Fred asked, turning his peaked cap in his fingers before jamming it onto his head.

'He's asleep.'

'I thought he might be interested to know that my stepdad's looking for a mechanic. Bert's got his own garage and a kinder man you'll never meet. You mentioned once that your husband trained in that?'

'Thank you, Fred. You're very kind. I'll let Paul know.' Annie was delighted. A real, proper job all above board and not only that, it sounded as if no one suspected Paul's part in last night's drama.

She saw Paul vanish from the doorway as Fred turned to go. Fred's gaze flickered to the bedroom and she was suddenly certain he knew that Paul was there, listening.

'Bert's expecting him today. I was a bit cheeky and told him about Paul. When Bert heard of his war service he said he'd be proud to have him. It's a reputable garage so employees have to keep their noses clean, if you know what I mean.'

'I do,' Annie said and when her eyes locked with Fred's, they shared a moment of perfect understanding.

Fred could never say that he knew that Paul was involved in the warehouse break-in and neither could Annie confess to it. But he was offering Paul a second chance and if he messed it up or threw it away then all bets were off. Annie was determined that wouldn't happen. She reckoned Paul had had a real scare the evening before and would be only too glad to get work in Bert's garage.

When Fred had left, Paul came out and Annie rushed into his arms. They stood together, wordless and let their bodies do the talking. Feeling Paul's mouth press onto hers, she felt all her worries evaporating into the morning air.

'Can you look after Davey for a wee while? There's something I have to ask Elsie,' Annie said when they stopped kissing.

Elsie was at home as her shift started later and she smiled at Annie.

'Fred's been and told me all the shenanigans from last night. Doris was so brave and they caught Archie Bale. He deserves all he gets. That black marketeering is plain wrong and people like my ma got caught up in it. He sold her alcohol that ultimately killed her. He didn't force it down her throat but to my mind he's still guilty. If Ma hadn't got it from him, maybe she'd still be here.'

'I'm glad it's all over,' Annie agreed. 'We'll have to hear Doris's story at our knitting club. Elsie…'

'If it's about the sketch, I destroyed it. Your Paul's suffered enough with his war injury. As far as I'm concerned, that's an end to it.'

Annie wasn't given much to hugs but she leaned right in and hugged Elsie fervently.

Back at home, Paul was carrying Davey in his one good arm and telling him a story. Annie enjoyed watching them before they knew she was back. She took Davey and put him in his pram where he could wriggle and stare at his parents happily.

'I've been a daft laddie,' Paul said, when she turned to him.

'More than that,' Annie said. She had to get through to him how serious it was. 'It has to be over. You could have gone to jail, leaving me and Davey on our own.'

'It is over. I promise you, Annie. It's done. Archie's gone and so is the temptation to make easy money. I'm taking Constable Cooper's offer of the job at the garage and I'm gonnac make something of myself. I don't understand why he did that for me.'

'He's a kind man, is Fred Cooper. He's a good friend.'

Paul stiffened. 'Women can't have male friends,' he growled.

'Och, keep your breeks on. He is just that. There's only one man for me and that's you, Paul Thom.' Annie kissed him fiercely to make her point.

'Aye, well. I don't want him hanging around here any more in any case. You tell him that next time he chaps the door.'

'I will,' Annie promised.

Paul frowned. 'The younger night watchman saw me, I'd swear he did. I tried to stop Archie from swinging a punch at the both of them and the moonlight made it all clear as day.'

'Doris is pals with Roy. I'll bet she's asked him to keep his mouth shut. We owe our friends so much I don't know how we'll ever repay them.'

'I've been lucky.'

'*We've* been lucky,' Annie corrected him. 'We're in this together. We might have lost our way for a while but our marriage is solid and things are going to get better for us from now on.'

Paul's dark eyes twinkled and Annie felt a rush of love and physical attraction for this man who finally looked and acted like the Paul she had fallen in love with at the start. No marriage was ever plain sailing but now she was sure they were stronger than ever.

'Well,' Paul said. 'I'd best get cleaned up and head over to the garage and hope that Fred Cooper's stepdad likes what he sees.'

# Chapter Nineteen

Doris had hardly slept the night before, her mind full of the canal drama and when she did sleep, her dreams were of giant keys and looming dark figures. The police had been kind but they had asked a lot of questions and she had had to describe the events several times before they were satisfied and left. In spite of all that, and her asthma attack on the towpath, she leapt out of bed in the morning full of wired energy and ate a quick breakfast.

'Back to bed with you,' Leila fussed, scooping extra porridge into Doris's breakfast bowl.

'I'm not hungry and I'm not tired either,' Doris said, pushing the bowl away.

'Oh dear. Are you ill? I'm not surprised after what happened last night. You really have to take care with your chest, dear. I sent a message for the factory with Elsie to say you won't be going in today.'

'Why did you do that? I'm fine, Mum. I really am. I'm stronger than you think.'

Leila looked so distressed that Doris didn't say any more. Her mum was never going to understand that she was capable of looking after herself. She put on her cardigan and buttoned it up.

'Where are you going?' Leila cried.

'I've got something to do that can't wait,' Doris said. If she didn't have to be at Fearnmore until tomorrow then she had time to sort some things out.

She walked smartly out of their flat and across the landing where she knocked on Mr Gibb's door. He opened it cautiously. Doris stood there, hands on hips and feeling completely calm.

'Good morning, Mr Gibb. I'd like you to clear your garden equipment out of the Anderson shelter please. That shelter isn't just for you, it's for me and my mum, too. If you don't move that stuff this morning then I'll be doing it for you. And while you're at it, you can move the blankets and oil lamps back in. Those are for your comfort as well as ours if there's a raid.'

His mouth opened in an 'O' of surprise. Doris turned smartly on her heel but stopped.

'And another thing,' she said over her shoulder on her way out of the close, 'You leave my mum's flowers and veg alone. I don't want to see them weeded out and chucked on the path or I'll be back to have words with you.'

She didn't wait for an answer but clattered down the steps and up into Roy's close. Oh, but she felt strong! She had got the best of a baddie last night and Mr Gibb was nothing compared to that. Now, she had to see Roy before this euphoria wore off. She had to know what that kiss meant. Even if Roy hadn't meant it, she needed to know. Right now, she could deal with that.

'Dor, there you are. I was coming over to find you.' Roy came out of the flat before she raised her fist to knock on the door. 'Come on, let's walk. It's chaos in there.' Beyond him, Christine's shrieks and Mrs Allen's yells confirmed it.

Doris felt self-conscious as he adjusted his stride to hers and they walked along Kiltie Street in the direction of the canal. It was nippy out and she shivered in her cardigan and skirt. Roy took off his coat and put it round her shoulders. With a ripple of delight, she snuggled into it, smelling his scent of Woodbines and Lifebuoy soap on the wool.

'You were brave last night.' Roy glanced across at her. 'If you hadn't let me and Hugh out, they'd have got away with stealing a lot of goods.'

'I wasn't brave. I just did what had to be done. Anyone would have done the same.'

'Naw, you're wrong. Plenty of folk might have looked the other way or been too scared to find that key. You're a real heroine, Doris Connelly, and you'll just have to accept that.' Roy grinned.

Doris blushed. The heat in her cheeks deepened when Roy took her hand in his. They walked along like a real couple, hand in hand. She had to ask him.

'How's Violet?'

'I hope she's very well but I don't know. Haven't heard from her and don't expect to.'

'But you and she…' Doris murmured.

'Violet's a lovely girl but we both knew it wasn't meant to last and we only dated until she got her move south again.'

'Oh.' She kept her gaze on her feet. Her shoes were clumpy utility issue and she wished she had little bows on the toes to make them pretty. Her lisle stockings wrinkled at her ankles but she couldn't very well pull them up. She was conscious then of her thick-lensed specs and her hair which never held a curl and couldn't take the fashionable hairstyles. She might as well admit it. She was no catch for Roy. But she couldn't help asking anyway.

'Last night… when I unlocked the office and untied you… you…' She almost lost her courage but remembered that if she was able to outwit Archie Bale and tell Mr Gibb what to do, she had this. 'You kissed me.'

She stopped, hugging herself in Roy's thick woollen working man's coat, and looked across at him. Roy was smiling a daft sort of smile. He reached out and stroked her hair with a roughened finger.

'I did, didn't I? What a cheek.'

'Why did you?' Doris said, when he didn't go on.

Now it was Roy's turn to look at his shoes. She couldn't believe it. It was almost as if he was shy. Roy Allen, who sang and whistled and called out confidently to all his friends and neighbours and who would lift a hand to help anyone, seemed lost for words.

'Roy? If it was a mistake, it's all right. Really. It was a strange situation—'

'It wasn't a mistake. It was the opposite.' Roy's head shot up and she felt the full blast of his blue eyes on hers.

'You wanted to kiss me?' Doris asked, incredulously.

'Don't sound so shocked. You don't know how clever and beautiful you are. I've wanted to kiss you for a long time but we're friends, you and me. I was scared we'd lose that if we stepped out and it went wrong. Besides, why would you choose me? I can't even read properly. The letters wriggle around like tadpoles on the page.'

'But you know so much more than me about history and the world and politics. I like reading but I've a lot to learn.'

'Looks like I have a lot to learn too,' Roy whispered and he leaned right in and kissed her.

Doris's mouth opened under the gentle pressure of his mouth and she gave herself up to the pleasure of the kiss which deepened until she felt a thrill throughout her whole body and an ache of need which made her step in close to him until their bodies moulded together. With a groan, Roy stepped back.

'We're never going to lose our friendship,' Doris said shakily, her lips tender and tingling. 'Whatever happens.'

'In that case, I accept your offer of stepping out,' Roy said.

'Och, you're teasing me now.'

'Sorry, Dor. I couldn't resist. Come to that, I can't resist you at all. Give us another kiss.'

When they came up for air, Roy took a deep breath and dropped to his knees. 'Doris Connelly, will you do me the honour of becoming my wife?'

'Roy, what are you doing? Get up before your knees get wet.'

'Not until you give me the right answer. But hurry, 'cos you're right. The grass is fair swampy down here.'

'I'd love to marry you. Yes, please,' Doris beamed.

Roy got up and they embraced. Doris laid her head on his shoulder, realising where they were now. The canal was within sight.

'I've been following you here on my Wednesday evenings just to make sure you're all right and for the joy of seeing you whistling and walking, all jaunty, like.'

'I know.'

'Why didn't you say something?' she was mortified.

'And spoil your fun? No, it was fine the way it was. Besides, if I was lucky, you sometimes came and chatted to me and made my evening. Those days, I was singing inside even when old Hugh was grumpy.' Roy laughed.

'When will we get married?' Doris asked.

'As soon as possible if it's down to me. I'd have to ask the bride, though. It's usually up to her and her mother.'

'God, I'd forgotten about Mum. She's going to fuss over all the details and drive me mad.'

'Let her if she'll enjoy it. We've got each other, Dor, and that's all that matters. If your ma wants to sort out the details, well, that's fine. Anyway, my ma will chip in too and no doubt Christine will insist on being a bridesmaid.'

Doris grinned. It hadn't struck her until Roy pointed it out that she was gaining a large family. How wonderful it was going to be. It wasn't just her and Mum any more and she was going to enjoy being a part of the boisterous Allen clan. With luck, there would be wee Allens to increase their numbers. She blushed and glanced at Roy who was now whistling a merry tune. She was going to be Mrs Doris Allen!

–

It felt like the whole of Kiltie Street had turned out to say goodbye. Annie and Paul's belongings had gone on ahead so they only had two suitcases and the pram to take to the station. She had tried to give the pram back to the Woodleys but Jeannie had refused it. Their Dennis wasn't one to sit in a pram these days, she'd said. Annie was to keep it as a going away gift.

Jeannie came across now. 'I can't believe you're moving away. I haven't seen you as much as I should this year. Our lives have drifted apart but I wish you well.'

Annie nodded. It seemed like a long while since she had just given birth to Davey and Jeannie had visited, leaving Annie restless and envious of her friend's life of work and dancing. Now she realised just how lucky she was being married to Paul and mother to a healthy, happy seven-month-old boy who was getting bigger every day. She was too busy to miss working at the factory and her friendship with Elsie and Doris had made up for losing her old friends such as Jeannie and Eileen.

'I wish you all the best too and hope that Bill comes back home again soon.' She knew Bill had been back on leave once or twice that year as she'd seen him in the street.

'Actually, I have a secret that I'm going to share with you as you're leaving but you have to promise not to tell anyone. I'm pregnant.' Jeannie's eyes shone happily as she whispered in Annie's ear.

'That's wonderful news. So, you will be wanting the pram back sooner than I thought,' Annie teased.

Jeannie laughed and Annie joined in. Jeannie winked and drew back to be with the other neighbours watching from their doorsteps as Elsie and Doris came over. Beyond them, Paul was in conversation with Fred Cooper and Martin O'Leary and Annie thought proudly how well he held himself, as if all his pride and vigour had returned. There were no more whisky bottles in their home these days and Paul rarely went to the pub. He was happier at home with his beautiful wife and great wee son, he said.

'So, you're away,' Doris said. 'But you'll be back for my wedding, won't you?'

'I wouldn't miss it for the world. But it's not until spring – or did you change your mind?'

'It's still spring but Mum's fretting over whether we can get nice flowers then or if we should wait 'til summer. Roy's very patient whenever she announces the next problem but I doubt he'll want to wait that long.' Doris unconsciously stretched out her left hand where a small diamond ring glinted in the cold December sunlight.

'How's your mum?' Elsie asked Annie.

Ivy had fallen over a brick in the blackout and twisted her ankle a few weeks ago. While the ankle had healed, her confidence had not and she seemed to be slipping back into being an invalid when Annie had suggested she and Paul come to live with her.

'She's much brighter now she knows we're coming for real,' Annie said. 'I'll miss Kiltie Street but Mum needs me, even if she doesn't know it.'

'We'll miss you,' Elsie said. 'Knitting club night won't be the same without you when it's just me and Doris.'

'I'll miss the both of youse too but Dumbarton's not that far away so we can visit each other. I might even come up for the knitting 'cos Mum will be there to look after Davey. You're not getting rid of me that easily.'

'Everything's changed, though,' Elsie said, sounding wistful. 'You're moving away, Doris is getting married and Jessie is up north with the Cranstons.'

Annie felt bad for Elsie. Her plans to live with her father hadn't worked out and when Doris got married she'd have Roy as her focus and not her friends.

'Come and visit me soon. Both of you,' she said. 'We'll have afternoon tea like posh folk. That is, if I can get any butter or make mock cream.'

Flakes of snow began to fall and the neighbours waved and went back indoors. Annie waved to Elsie and Doris as Paul called over that they should go.

'Dammit, I forgot my work boots. I'll only be a minute,' Paul said, jogging away back into the close.

Annie stood rocking the pram. Fred Cooper came over. He was in uniform and on his beat but had stopped in to wish them all the best.

'Bert's very pleased with Paul's work at the garage,' Fred said.

'We're so thankful to you for getting him that job,' Annie replied, watching the snowflakes melt on his dark blue uniform jacket and wondering if they were doing the same to her new second-hand blue felt hat.

'I wish you all the best. I'll miss you,' Fred said as if she hadn't spoken. 'I've always admired you, Annie.'

'Constable Cooper… Fred… can I speak plainly? You may admire me but I'm a married woman and I love my husband. I've never felt for another man what I feel for Paul nor will I ever. There's someone special for you who doesn't live a stone's throw from where we are standing right now and you're missing what's under your nose.'

Fred looked startled but Annie only smiled. She'd said her piece and it was up to him to work it out now.

—

Ivy was pleased to see them when they arrived at the cosy flat above the greengrocer's shop in Dumbarton. She was wearing a fresh housecoat and had covered her hair in a green turban. She took Davey and bounced him in her arms with a big smile until the baby chuckled and curled in to her lovingly.

'The pram can stay out on the landing. I've got the teapot warming and I've made a prune pudding.'

Annie stood awkwardly inside the flat with Paul behind her. 'Where will we put the suitcases?' Had they made the wrong decision, coming here to live? Ivy's flat seemed smaller than ever and Annie remembered the mattress in the parlour only too clearly. And where were the rest of their belongings?

'Paul will take them up to your bedroom, won't you, son?' Ivy said calmly.

'But there's only the two bedrooms…' Annie faltered.

'Aye, that's right. One for me and one for youse two.'

'And Brian?' Annie said with a lump in her throat.

'I think we both know that Brian's not coming home for a good, long stretch,' Ivy said and her black brows sagged until she summoned up a watery smile. 'I've moved his stuff under my bed in the meanwhile.'

'I'll take these up then,' Paul said hastily, clearly wanting to get away from women's emotions.

Ivy kissed Davey's head and looked at Annie over his soft tufts of hair. 'You were right, love. I was in denial about Brian. I wanted him home so badly. I'm sorry I made you and Paul sleep in the parlour last time round, that was wrong but I wasn't right in the head, I know I wasn't.'

'I wasn't trying to make you unhappy when I told you Brian wasn't coming home,' Annie said. 'I just wanted you to acknowledge it was true. It frightened me when you couldn't accept that, as if you were losing your mind.'

'I think I did lose it a wee bit, to be honest. But it comforted me to pretend he would be home soon.'

The two women went into the kitchen, which smelt of Mansion Polish and was neat and clean. Annie poured the tea while Ivy settled Davey on a small rug on the floor with a cushion at his back and well away from the range.

'How's Paul?' Ivy asked. 'I heard from Mrs Connelly about the odd goings-on at the canal in November but I'm that pleased he's got a job at the garage now.'

Annie hadn't told Ivy anything about that night but suddenly she wanted this fresh start to be just that. Fresh and not based on lies. She told her mother all that had happened with Archie Bale and how their second chance had come about. When she was finished, Ivy didn't speak and she was afraid they were going to be thrown out before they had even settled in.

'I'm glad you've told me. I suspected Paul was involved.'

'Mum, please—'

'—but I'm proud that he's got out of that life and has a respectable job. After all, he's Davey's dad and he's family.'

'Does that mean you'll try and get on with him better?' Annie said with relief.

'I'll try. I've no doubt him and me will rub up the wrong way sometimes but I can see you love the man and that's good enough for me.'

'Let me pop Davey up for a nap and I'll be back down for that tea,' Annie said. She took the sleepy baby from the floor and went up the narrow stairs, thinking that when Davey started to crawl they would have to stop him going up or down the stairs somehow.

She went into what she had always called Brian's bedroom. The moving men had put their double bed into it and the single bed had gone. She remembered how furious she'd been with Paul for buying it and wasting their money. Now, she saw it fondly as a memory of their Kiltie Street days. Their sideboard was in the room too which made it somewhat cramped but there was enough space for them to be comfortable here. The rest of the furniture had been rented so hadn't journeyed to Dumbarton.

Paul was lying resting on the bed. His eyes barely opened when she came in.

'All well with your ma?'

'Aye, she's fine. I told her the truth about you working with Archie Bale and it's water under the bridge. She's all for a fresh start and so am I. How's your arm. Is it still hurting?'

'My stump? No, it doesn't pain me so much now. I don't understand it but I'm not complaining. Give me my boy. He can sleep beside me while his ma and nana have a blether.'

'You're a good man, Paul Thom. But you can't escape Mum's prune pudding forever. Give me a wee hour with her to catch her up and then I'll be fetching you for tea.' Annie poked his stomach jokingly. Paul caught her fingers in his and kissed them. Then he tucked Davey into his side and closed his eyes.

Downstairs, Ivy had produced a plate of scones which she pushed towards Annie.

'Would you like me to take you to visit Brian in prison?' Annie said as she sat down. The notion had just come to her as a way of keeping Ivy cheered up.

'Would you do that for me?' Ivy said, brows high with surprise. 'It's an awful long way south.'

'Of course I'll do it. Davey should meet his Uncle Brian. It'll be an adventure for us.'

'Even if they release him, I don't think he'll come back here to live,' Ivy sighed. 'The army might not have suited him but he liked being abroad. Remember, he used to talk about the foreign food and the language and the civilians he met? He had itchy feet even when he was hiding in the hills and coming down to the house after dark. I don't see him settling in that room upstairs. Not now.'

'Let's deal with that when it happens. We'll make the most of our wee family just now and cope with whatever comes,' Annie said.

'Do you know, Annie Thom, I do believe you have finally grown up. And I'm that proud of you, so I am.'

# Chapter Twenty

Dear Elsie

*I'm writing this while tucked up in the snug by the bay window in my room. Mrs Potter has brought me a cup of cocoa and I can see the snow falling outside in the garden. How are you? I'm imagining you in our room, your feet on our rag rug while you sit on the bed reading this letter. Auntie Alison asked to be remembered to you and sends her kind regards.*

*I've learnt how to ride my new bicycle and I'm so fast now into the village to pick up the messages for Mrs Potter. She's says she doesn't know how she managed without me. Also I'm not to call them 'messages' any more, I've to say 'groceries'. Uncle Donald showed me how to fix a puncture and I'm allowed to go out all day with a sandwich as long as I'm home before dark. Of course it gets dark so early that I'm home long before dinner. That's another word for tea. They have lunch at dinner-time and tea in the afternoon before dinner and sometimes we have toast for supper. It's confusing! It's cold up here, I wonder if it's cold in Glasgow too.*

*I'm that excited, Uncle and Auntie say I can stay on at school after next year. I want to be a teacher. I bet I'll be the first girl from Kiltie Street to do that! Uncle Donald says we'll have a real tree for Christmas. There'll be candles on it and little glass baubles and Mrs Potter is going to make shortbread shapes to hang on it too. With my pocket money I've bought handkerchiefs for Auntie Alison and Mrs Potter and tobacco for Uncle Donald. Auntie Alison has posted a parcel to you, I hope you get it all right. It's from all of us. I don't want to give away the surprise but I knitted your present from me, I hope you like it. Don't open your parcel until Christmas Day when I can think of you.*

*Are you coming to visit soon? Auntie Alison says the trains are awful just now but there's a bus comes to the village, maybe you can catch it from Glasgow?*

*As always, your loving wee sister, Jessie.*

Elsie blinked away tears as she finished reading her sister's letter. Jessie wrote faithfully every week about what she was doing and life in the Perthshire village. While Elsie loved getting the letters, with each one it felt as if Jessie was moving further and further away from her, from Kiltie Street and from her Glasgow roots. She didn't begrudge Jessie her good fortune but along with a relief that her wee sister was doing all right was a bittersweet sadness that their lives were going to be so very different as the future unfolded. Imagine, wee Jessie was going to be a teacher! And she could do it too, she was smart enough. If Ma had lived, there was no way Jessie would have been able to do that. There hadn't been the money. No, Jessie would have worked in a factory just like Elsie did, married some man and had weans and that would have been the end of it. Now she had opportunities to blossom under the kind care of the wealthy Cranstons.

It was the last Sunday before Christmas and Elsie was listless. Jessie's letter had left her even more unsettled and she was dreading the evening meal when Uncle Leo and Alice made their customary appearance. She knew Leo enjoyed the ticking down of the clock on her occupancy of the bedroom and he reminded her without fail that only so many weeks remained until he and Alice were to claim the room for their new son or daughter.

'Get yourself out and blow away the cobwebs, as Ma would say,' she told herself.

She took down her coat from the hook on the back of the bedroom door and shrugged it on. She didn't own any boots so her work shoes would have to do, in spite of the layer of snow that lay over the Maryhill landscape. She had her beret and gloves to keep the cold at bay and she put those on, ready for the weather outside.

Kiltie Street looked like a winter wonderland. The shapes of the cobbles, the usually muddy slope and the bench that overlooked it were all softened by the glinting white blanket as yet unsullied by cart wheels, although the local children had scooped it up to make a small snowman and throw the inevitable snowballs.

She trudged along the street, missing Annie and Doris. Annie had been as good as her word, coming back up for their knitting club evenings but it wasn't the same as knowing she was just a few doors down. She was glad her friend was happy and if she mentioned Paul and Davey every sentence that just made Elsie smile and share a wink with Doris.

As for Doris, she was starry-eyed and sang little tunes while she knitted furiously. She was now knitting not only for the troops and for Davey but for her bottom drawer. She had made blankets and clever table mats and a pot holder. What she hadn't shown them, but Elsie had glimpsed, was a pair of baby bootees and some tiny baby socks. She was sure Doris wasn't in the family way yet but clearly she had hopes and wishes for the following spring once she had married Roy.

And where did that leave her? Elsie sighed out loud where only the crows and jackdaws could hear her. Her friends' lives were sorted and they had bright futures ahead of them. Was she being selfish wanting the same? It seemed like all she had to look forward to was working at Fearnmore munitions factory and living with the Mearns until she was thrown out next March.

She should have been looking for a place to live somewhere else in Glasgow but she hadn't yet. She was worried about how she was going to manage to rent a place on her meagre wages. So she put it off. Aunt Norah reminded her in almost every letter of her offer of a home but so far she hadn't answered on that. Manchester was far away from Jessie, Annie and Doris.

Her thoughts turned swiftly to Fred Cooper but she blocked them. Fred wasn't interested in her except as a friend. He had been wonderful, helping when Davey was sick and when Jessie went missing and she had been so very grateful for his support and for listening when she was going to meet her father. But that was all it was. Friendship and nothing more. Her feet crunched on the snow, leaving patterns behind her. She caught the bus into the centre of town, not really thinking about much. The rhythm of the wheels, the noise of the engine and the smell of fumes along with the loud chatter of other passengers soothed her so that she looked out upon the Glasgow scenery without noticing much.

She got off and walked to George Square. Here the snow was almost gone and the traffic had dirtied what was left of it to brown sludge. She wandered around the shops in the nearby streets, looking into the windows with their Christmas displays. Mostly, they showed pictures of items that weren't available now but once the war was over they would be back. 'Something to look forward to!' cried one poster for Mackintosh's sweets, 'that day when a good old-fashioned Christmas again brings lots and lots of Mackintosh's'.

Around the square were colourful posters advertising the pantomimes that season. She had a choice of Puss in Boots at the Metropolitan, Red Riding Hood at the Alhambra or Robinson Crusoe at the Pavilion. She loved pantomime, Ma had taken them once years ago when Jessie was small and they had enjoyed the singing and shouting out. She wondered idly if Fred Cooper liked the panto. The jolliness of them was intended to shut out the horrible every day struggles but the sandbags outside the shops were a reminder that there was a war on, if she needed it, along with the taped windows against bomb blast.

Her presents were ready, all knitted in her evenings. She had made a scarf for Jessie and it was already wrapped in brown paper and string, ready to post. For Aunt Sarah there was a ration-card case and a string shopping bag. She had made egg-cosies for her grandmother and Aunt Ada. She had nothing for Uncle Leo and Alice but thought she wasn't likely to get a present from them either. Doris and Annie were going to receive small jars of bath salts. She had painted the jars to decorate them and cut up a hair ribbon to tie round each.

'Hey, missus. Gonnae gie us a copper for a brew?' A man with a grimy, straggling beard and a leg missing sat at the corner of the square. A sign in front of him said that he was a veteran of the Great War.

Elsie fumbled in her purse for a coin and put it into his stovepipe hat – a crumpled, smeared object that sat in front of his one splayed leg.

'I thank you kindly, young miss. There's many that pass by and don't stop. Aye, and think on all the young men in this bloody war that'll end up just like me. It's a crying shame, that's what it is.'

She shuddered as she walked on. She thought about Paul and his lost arm, about Annie's brother Brian who was imprisoned because he had been so traumatised he couldn't go back to fight. Then there was Jeannie's husband Bill away in Europe somewhere and her brother Jimmy who was fighting in Africa. So many friends and people she knew who were affected by the war. She had lost Jessie to it.

'Elsie!'

The call broke through her gloomy reverie and she looked up to see her father.

He was smiling tentatively at her. 'You were in a world of your own. How are you and Jessie?'

She saw the eagerness in his gaze and shied away from it. She had made it clear that she wanted nothing more to do with him so why was he approaching her now? But common decency made her answer.

'Jessie's away in Perthshire for the rest of the war so she's safe.'

'And you?'

'What do you care? You let us go. You let your wife decide we weren't worthy of living with you.' It burst out of her.

'I said I was sorry. I am sorry. I didn't want you to leave the way you did. You're my daughters, of course I care about you.'

'There's nothing to be done,' she said.

Michael Weir glanced away from her and then back. 'I can't force you to keep in touch but I hope that you do. You've got my Pladda Lane address. If you need money, please do get in touch. I meant what I said, about giving you enough to rent a place for yourself. Look after yourself, Elsie.'

She watched him hurry through the sparse crowd in the square. It wasn't busy because it was Sunday and the shops were all shut. The day was for people like her who only wished to window shop and couldn't afford to buy in any case. There were only five days until Christmas. She wasn't looking forward to the prospect of spending the celebration in the Mearns' flat. She looked at her father's back, getting smaller as he went away. Soon he'd be round the corner of a building and out of sight.

Before she knew what she was doing, Elsie was running, her hand pressing her hat down onto her head to stop it being lost.

'Dad! Stop!'

He looked back, puzzled, just before the end of the street and when he saw her speeding towards him, his expression lit up. Elsie puffed as she stopped, her cheeks flushed with the exertion.

'I wanted… I wanted to say, have a happy Christmas when it comes,' she said lamely.

Michael's smile crinkled his eyes. 'I wish you the same. Let me buy you lunch. Please, Elsie, I'd like to and you can tell me your holiday plans.'

She wasn't going to tell him all her plans but she found herself nodding. Was it a mistake? She didn't know but she felt hollow inside with Jessie and Annie gone and Doris busy with her life, and hovering over her always the knowledge that she was soon to be homeless. Her father had let her down but he was still her flesh and blood.

Michael led the way to a small corner café where a grumpy waitress took their order for two bowls of vegetable soup and told them there was a war on, didn't they know, when they asked for bacon rolls only to find there were none.

'Never mind, two bowls of soup and slices of bread, please,' Michael said politely.

The waitress grunted and clip-clopped away, her pencil tucked into her hair and a tired sag to her shoulders.

'This war's wearing everyone out,' he remarked.

He looked worn out too, Elsie thought as she gazed at him.

'Is everything all right?' she asked.

'We had a telegram. Timothy's missing in action. You'll probably have heard on the wireless about the bombing raids over Berlin. We think he was there. Annabelle's distraught, we both are.'

'I'm so sorry,' Elsie said.

'Thank you, my dear. It's difficult in the house at the moment so I try to get out and walk to clear my head.'

What about Annabelle? Elsie thought. Doesn't she need your support and for you to be there? It wasn't her business but it felt as if her father ran away whenever anything became difficult. He was never going to be what she needed: a source of advice and strength and help. She had to accept his limitations as a father if she was going to keep in touch with him. And she had decided now that she would. She was so alone as it was.

'There are reasons to be hopeful about this blasted war,' he said with forced cheerfulness. 'After all, we have Jerry on the run in Italy, the Russians are advancing steadily and our boys in blue are bombing northern Germany to smithereens. They say this will be our last wartime Christmas and I'm inclined to agree.'

Their soup and bread arrived and, while they ate, Elsie told Michael about Jessie and her home with the Cranstons in rural Perthshire. He was proud to hear Jessie was staying on at school and again promised money. This time, Elsie didn't refuse. Not on Jessie's behalf, anyway, as it would make all the difference to her sister's future. For herself, she didn't want any money.

Afterwards, Michael paid for the lunch and even managed to wheedle a smile out of their waitress by tipping her generously.

'Thank you for my dinner,' Elsie said as they stood outside the corner café, ready to go their separate ways. 'I'll write to you and let you know where to send the money for Jessie. I'll keep in touch.'

'That's all I ask,' Michael said and the grateful note in his voice made her feel guilty but strangely happy too. 'I have two lovely daughters and I've been a dreadful father, I know that. But it's not too late to turn a leaf, is it?'

'No, Dad, it's not too late. You'll write me back?'

'Of course, dear. But I hope you'll come and visit on occasion. Annabelle has her ladies' luncheons so perhaps then. We'll work it out.'

Elsie smiled inwardly. She'd be in the back door, so it seemed, rather than in the front as a daughter of the house would. Och well, it was better than nothing and all her father could bring himself to offer, given his relationship with his wife. Besides, she hadn't been entirely honest about her own plans. Because she knew now what she had to do.

She arrived back at the flat before Uncle Leo and Alice were due to arrive for the usual Sunday meal and helped her aunts to set the table and prepare the food. She also had time to go into her room and fill her suitcase with her clothes, ration book and other belongings. She put the filled suitcase on top of her bed and buckled it. She left her Christmas gifts on her table, wrapped and labelled. Jessie's was packed so she could post it as soon as possible. She tucked Aunt Norah's letters into her handbag and had a last look round. She would be sad to leave her rag rug after the hours it had taken to make but there wasn't room for it. She ran her fingers over the few pieces of furniture and remembered Doris and Roy's kindness in providing them.

She was going to travel to Manchester and take up Aunt Norah and Felicity's kind invitation to live with them. When she got there, she'd write to her supervisor at Fearnmore munitions factory and let them know she had gone. No doubt there were munitions factories in Manchester who would be pleased to take her on. She might even work with Aunt Norah at hers.

Although Jessie was up north and Elsie had thought she couldn't leave her, with every letter from her sister it was obvious that Jessie had settled in to that life and that soon, her loving Auntie Alison and Uncle Donald would want to adopt her. Elsie wasn't going to stand in their way. Jessie didn't need her any more. Very soon, Elsie was going to be homeless and the only place she had to go was to Aunt Norah.

Her feelings for Fred must surely disappear, especially if she wasn't going to see him again. She hoped that was true because when she thought of how he had hugged her, her body remembered only too well the thrill of it. It hurt that he liked Annie better than her. Elsie lifted her chin and set a smile to her lips. No one was going to see she was hurting. She was going to go for afternoon tea with her relatives and be polite and then slip away without them noticing. Her only regret was Aunt Sarah, who had been so kind all these months. She'd write later to explain.

In the end, it didn't go quite to plan. Leo and Alice arrived with Leo complaining about the bitter weather and the snow holding them up. Alice's baby bump was very visible under her loose fur-trimmed coat as she was nearly seven months gone and she was ushered to a chair by Aunt Sarah and urged to rest.

'Don't fuss so, Sarah. My wife is fine,' Leo snapped.

Aunt Sarah drew back, flustered, and Elsie tried to remain calm and fight the urge to knock her Uncle Leo's head from his shoulders. What a horrible man he was.

'What have you got us for tea today, Ada?' Leo rubbed his hands together.

His paunch showed that rationing wasn't having an effect in his household and Elsie wondered if there was another Archie Bale in Dennistoun dealing with people like her uncle who selfishly didn't want to do without, even during the war.

Ada sighed, her lips pinched. 'I could list what you can't have. I do declare the butcher and greengrocer have taken against me, they had nothing. So it's devilled fish coated with oatmeal you'll be having, with Brown Betty for afters which is more breadcrumbs than apples and there's no syrup in it either.'

Uncle Leo's face dropped but he managed a spirited, 'Well, well, that sounds lovely.'

Isobel was helped to the table by Sarah and sat watching with an eagle eye as Elsie helped Ada to serve up. Leo waited until Elsie had served his plate of fish and offered him boiled cabbage and they were all seated and eating before glancing at her and then to Isobel.

'Alice is keen to decorate the room for the baby, Mother. When might we have it?'

Isobel looked startled. 'We agreed that Elspeth and Jessie had six months to find new lodgings and that you would have the room once the baby was born so I expected you to take it on next March.'

'As Jessie has already gone, it seems to me we can make that sooner,' Leo said. 'It would be nice to paint the bedroom and put in a new carpet so that it's ready.'

'What about Elsie? Where is she to go?' Aunt Sarah asked bravely.

Uncle Leo threw her a withering glance and didn't deign to answer. At the head of the table, Isobel looked undecided. Aunt Ada carefully separated a fish bone from her food and put it on the edge of her plate. Elsie couldn't stand it any longer. She jumped up and put down her cutlery with a clang.

'It doesn't matter because I'm leaving right this minute. Aunt Ada, you'll have to wash up the dishes all by yourself for once. Grandmother, I won't bother to write as you don't care about me. Aunt Sarah, you've been the only kindness in this house and I won't forget you.'

'You can't simply walk out of here. Where will you go? I demand you tell me!' Isobel cried, her bony knuckles tightening across the top of her walking stick.

'That's just it. I *can* simply walk out of here. Watch me do it,' Elsie replied.

With five pairs of eyes watching, she turned on her heel, out of the kitchen away from the smells of fish and cabbage, grabbed her suitcase, gas mask and coat and was down the stairs before any of them had moved. Her heart was thudding in her chest and she had a desperate desire to giggle as she half ran along Kiltie Street to catch the bus to Central Station. She had no idea if there was a train to Manchester so late in the day but it didn't matter. She'd take a ticket south and if she had to stop somewhere overnight, so be it. She'd be with her fascinating Aunt Norah and Felicity very soon.

It was if a heavy weight had lifted from her as soon as she left the flat. Her mood soared and dipped in equal measures as she felt the freedom of it all combined with the emotions of leaving Glasgow and Doris and Annie, Aunt Sarah and most of all, Fred.

–

Over in the railway cottages, Fred was sitting waiting for his evening meal. His shift at the yard had been an early one so he was in his civvies listening to the wireless. In the kitchen, he heard the clatter of plates as his mum prepared the food. He couldn't concentrate on the wireless music so got up and turned it off. Annie's words kept echoing in his head. *There's someone special for you who doesn't live a stone's throw from where we are standing right now and you're missing what's under your nose.*

He had thought a lot about those words over the past few weeks but he had held back from visiting Elsie. He had also thought a lot about her – her pretty face, the way her blonde curls swept back from her cheekbones, how tall and slender she was and how much he admired her blue eyes. He had mistaken the easy way they chatted with one another for friendship. Or perhaps he hadn't wanted to admit to himself that it was more. A lot more. Holding her in his arms, however innocently, had made him realise how much he wanted to kiss her. So what was holding him back? And why did he have a dreadful sense that he had to find her right this minute?

'Mum, I've got to go out,' he shouted, grabbing his coat from the back of the chair where he had slung it earlier.

'Now?' Monica's face appeared round the kitchen entrance. 'I'll keep your tea in the oven for you.' She took the sight of him in and nodded with satisfaction. 'I see you've come to your senses, then.'

'What?'

'Don't play the daft laddie with me, son. Just don't come back here alone this evening. You'd best hurry.' She kissed his cheek and pushed him none too gently towards the front door of the cottage.

And he did hurry, some sixth sense hurtling him forward, afraid he'd never see her again if he didn't rush. Her aunt's sour face at the Kiltie Street door, shaking her head. No, they had no idea where she was. No, they didn't expect her back. Good riddance too – after all they had done for her, this was how she had repaid them. He didn't wait to answer but ran back outside onto the street, looking this way and that. Where could she have gone?

He knocked at the Connellys and Doris answered. She didn't waste time. She told him about Elsie's other aunt and her offer of a home. Doris was certain that Elsie must have fled to go there. If Fred found at her at the station, he was to let them know. *Yes, yes, all that could wait.* The world had coalesced into a small halo of images and sounds around his head as his heartbeat cried *Elsie, Elsie* and he prayed he wasn't too late.

–

Central Station's Victorian grandeur was lost on Fred as he raced into the main concourse and looked for her. Even though it was a Sunday, it was fairly busy with servicemen and women with kit bags and people with suitcases and small children. He saw her standing under the station clock. She was quite still, staring ahead at the noticeboard, her suitcase at her feet and a red beret on her blonde hair like a beacon of hope in the sea of dark winter coats. It took all his courage to approach her and he realised he wasn't quite free of what Alice had done to him yet. But he wasn't going to lose this woman because of that. Elsie was worth fighting for.

He called her name and saw her frown. Then she turned and saw him. Fred broke into a run, dignity forgotten, and before he lost his nerve, he kissed her. She clung to him and returned his kiss with a passion that surprised and delighted him. He didn't want their kiss to stop. Ever.

Elsie felt as if she was dreaming. Fred was here and he was kissing her. How was that possible? It was as if she had conjured him up, like a magic trick, she'd been thinking so hard about him. She cupped his head to kiss him again, feeling the strong cords of muscle at the back of his neck and the heat of his body.

'I thought it was Annie you liked,' she said, dazed, as they drew slightly apart.

'I like Annie but I'm in love with you,' he said simply. 'I'm a fool. It took me so long to understand what I was feeling. I didn't want to be in love because I was engaged once and it ended badly. I thought I couldn't love again but it turns out I was wrong. I love you.'

'Oh, Fred. I love you too. I was so sad waiting here for my train, knowing I'd likely never see you again.'

'Mum says I've not to come home tonight without you. Will you come with me?'

'I bought a ticket to the borders.' She held it up helplessly. 'I couldn't get all the way to Manchester tonight so I was going to stay in a hotel or a guest house and then journey on down.'

'You can stay with us tonight. Mum will sort something out so it's all proper, like. And tomorrow I'll help you find somewhere to live until we can get married. You will marry me, won't you?'

'Yes, Fred, I will marry you.' Elsie kissed him again and all the ghosts of the past faded away until there was only the two of them, ready to trust each other and love each other through these war years and on into a brighter future together.

# A letter from Carol

Dear Reader

I hope you are well. Thank you so much for choosing to read *Elsie's Wartime Wish* which is the second in the Kiltie Street Girls series (after *Jeannie's War*). I'm very grateful that you have chosen to read it and I hope that you have enjoyed it.

I wanted to write about some of the minor characters from *Jeannie's War* and found myself wondering about Elspeth (known to her family and friends as Elsie) who took the bus with Jeannie to the Fearnmore factory each day. I was also interested to see what happened to Annie who was so desperately keen on Paul by the end of the first book. And I have to admit to a soft spot for Doris, with her clumsiness and poor eyesight. She ended up surprising me with her strength of character.

If all that sounds like they are real people, it really feels like they are! The characters begin with a quick sketch and description but as I write and the chapters take shape, they come alive and don't always stick to the plan that I've drafted. That's the fun of writing stories.

If you enjoyed *Elsie's Wartime Wish*, I would be very grateful to hear your thoughts via a review, which will then allow other readers to find and read it. Reader reviews are very rewarding and very much appreciated.

Thank you for your support for my book and I hope that you will continue to follow me as I write the third story about the Kiltie Street Girls which focusses on Kathy, Jeannie's wayward sister.

You can get in touch on my social media pages on Twitter and Facebook.

Best wishes and happy reading

Carol x

Facebook link www.facebook.com/carolcmaclean
Twitter link www.twitter.com/carolcmaclean

# Acknowledgments

Thank you to the amazing Hera team, especially Keshini Naidoo for her enthusiasm and support, and Jennie Ayres for her thorough editing, all of which have made this a better book.

Special thanks to Alastair Dinsmor, Curator at the Glasgow Police Museum, for his invaluable help with Fred's uniform and duties and for answering my many questions about special constables and the police force in Glasgow during the second world war (any mistakes are my own of course).

Thank you also to the fabulous Romantic Novelists' Association for its wealth of information, support and friendships. Finally, thanks to my family for their encouragement and for giving me time to write.